Department of Health

Care Homes for Adults (18–65)

and

Supplementary Standards for Care Homes Accommodating Young People Aged 16 and 17

National Minimum Standards

Care Homes Regulations

February 2003

London: TSO

Published by TSO (The Stationery Office) and available from:

Online
www.tso.co.uk/bookshop

Mail, Telephone, Fax & E-mail
TSO
PO Box 29, Norwich, NR3 1GN
Telephone orders/General enquiries: 0870 600 5522
Fax orders: 0870 600 5533
E-mail: book.orders@tso.co.uk
Textphone 0870 240 3701

TSO Shops
123 Kingsway, London, WC2B 6PQ
020 7242 6393 Fax 020 7242 6394
68-69 Bull Street, Birmingham B4 6AD
0121 236 9696 Fax 0121 236 9699
9-21 Princess Street, Manchester M60 8AS
0161 834 7201 Fax 0161 833 0634
16 Arthur Street, Belfast BT1 4GD
028 9023 8451 Fax 028 9023 5401
18-19 High Street, Cardiff CF10 1PT
029 2039 5548 Fax 029 2038 4347
71 Lothian Road, Edinburgh EH3 9AZ
0870 606 5566 Fax 0870 606 5588

TSO Accredited Agents
(see Yellow Pages)

and through good booksellers

Published with the permission of the Department of Health
on behalf of the Controller of Her Majesty's Stationery Office.

First published 2002
Second edition 2003

ISBN 0 11 322608 X

Web Access

This document is available on the DoH internet website at:
http://www.doh.gov.uk/ncsc

Printed in the United Kingdom for the Stationery Office

National Minimum Standards for Care Homes for Adults (18–65) and Supplementary Standards for Care Homes Accommodating Young People Aged 16 and 17

A statement of national minimum standards published by the Secretary of State for Health under section 23(1) of the Care Standards Act 2000.

February 2003

An earlier version of this document was first published in December 2001 under the title:
Care Homes for Younger Adults and Adult Placements
National Minimum Standards

Care Homes Regulations

National Minimum Standards for Care Homes for Adults (18–65)

Note

This document contains a statement of national minimum standards published by the Secretary of State under section 23(1) of the Care Standards Act 2000. The statement is applicable to care homes (as defined by section 3 of that Act) which provide accommodation, together with nursing or personal care, for adults (aged 18 -65).

The statement includes the additional standards for children aged 16 or 17 who are service users in care homes.

The statement is accompanied, for explanatory purposes only, by an introduction to the statement as a whole, and a further introduction to each group of standards.

Each individual standard is numbered and consists of the numbered heading and numbered paragraphs. Each standard is, for explanatory purposes only, preceded by a title and an indication of the intended outcome in relation to that standard.

Department of Health

Contents

General Introduction

This document contains the Care Homes Regulations, National Minimum Standards for Care Homes for Adults (18–65) and Supplementary Standards for children aged 16 and 17 in Care Homes.

Together with the National Minimum Standards for Care Homes for Older People, these regulations and standards form the basis of the new regulatory framework under the Care Standards Act 2000 (CSA) for the conduct of care homes.

The regulations and standards included in this document have been drafted following consultation with service users, providers and regulators. They also take account of the outcome of the recent consultation on proposed amendments to certain environmental standards.

National Minimum Standards are issued by the Secretary of State for Health, but it is the responsibility of the National Care Standards Commission to apply them through regulation to the circumstances of individual establishments, agencies and institutions. The Commission will therefore advise on the standards' application in particular circumstances. Other queries – for example about the policies behind the standards – can be addressed to the Department of Health at this e-mail address: dhmail@ doh. gsi. gov. uk.

Note: the Regulations printed here have been edited so as to incorporate amendments made by S.I. 2002 No. 865.

STATUTORY INSTRUMENTS

2001 No. 3965

SOCIAL CARE, ENGLAND
CHILDREN AND YOUNG PERSONS, ENGLAND

The Care Homes Regulations 2001

Made	*11th December 2001*
Laid before Parliament	*12th December 2001*
Coming into force	*1st April 2002*

ARRANGEMENT OF REGULATIONS

PART I
GENERAL

PART II
REGISTERED PERSONS

PART III
CONDUCT OF CARE HOMES

The Secretary of State, in exercise of the powers conferred upon him by sections 3(3), 22(1), (2)(a) to (d) and (f) to (j), (5), (7)(a) to (h), (j) and (l), 25(1), 34(1), 35 and 118(5) to (7) of the Care Standards Act 2000[1], and of all other powers enabling him in that behalf, having consulted such persons as he considers appropriate[2], hereby makes the following Regulations:

PART I

GENERAL

Citation, commencement and extent

1. - (1) These Regulations may be cited as the Care Homes Regulations 2001 and shall come into force on 1st April 2002.

(2) These Regulations extend to England only.

Interpretation

2. - (1) In these Regulations -

"the Act" means the Care Standards Act 2000;
"environmental health authority" means the authority responsible for environmental health for the area in which the care home is situated;
"fire authority", in relation to a care home, means the authority discharging in the area in which the care home is situated the function of fire authority under the Fire Services Act 1947[3];
"general practitioner" means a registered medical practitioner who -

(a) provides general medical services under Part II of the National Health Service Act 1977[4];

(b) performs personal medical services in connection with a pilot scheme under the National Health Service (Primary Care) Act 1997[5]; or

(c) provides services which correspond to services provided under Part II of the National Health Service Act 1977, otherwise than in pursuance of that Act;

"health care professional" means a person who is registered as a member of any profession to which section 60(2) of the Health Act 1999[6] applies or who is clinical psychologist, child psychotherapist or speech therapist;
"inspection report" means a report prepared in relation to the care home under section 32(5) of the Act;
"organisation" means a body corporate or any unincorporated association other than a partnership;

"registered manager", in relation to a care home, means a person who is registered under Part II of the Act as the manager of the care home;

"registered person", in relation to a care home, means any person who is the registered provider or registered manager in respect of the care home;

"registered provider", in relation to a care home, means a person who is registered under Part II of the Act as a person carrying on the care home;

"relative", in relation to any person, means -

(a) the person's spouse;

(b) any parent, grandparent, child, grandchild, brother, sister, uncle, aunt, nephew or niece of his or his spouse;

(c) the spouse of any relative within sub-paragraph (b) of this definition,

and for the purpose of determining any such relationship a person's step-child shall be treated as his child, and references to "spouse" in relation to any person include a former spouse and a person who is living with the person as husband and wife;

"representative" means, in relation to a service user, a person, other than the registered person or a person employed at the care home, who with the service user's express or implied consent takes an interest in the service user's health and welfare;

"responsible individual" shall be construed in accordance with regulation 7(2)(c)(i);

"service user" means any person accommodated in the care home who is in need of nursing or personal care by reason of disability, infirmity, past or present illness, past or present mental disorder or past or present dependence on alcohol or drugs;

"service user's guide" means the written guide produced in accordance with regulation 5(1);

"service user's plan" means the written plan prepared in accordance with regulation 15(1);

"staff" means persons employed by the registered person to work at the care home but does not include a volunteer or a person employed under a contract for services;

"statement of purpose" means the written statement compiled in accordance with regulation 4(1).

(2) In these Regulations, unless the context otherwise requires, a reference -

(a) to a numbered regulation or Schedule is to the regulation in, or Schedule to, these Regulations bearing that number;

(b) in a regulation or Schedule to a numbered paragraph is to the paragraph in that regulation or Schedule bearing that number;

(c) in a paragraph to a lettered or numbered sub-paragraph is to the sub-paragraph in that paragraph bearing that letter or number.

(3) In these Regulations, references to employing a person include employing a person whether or not for payment and whether under a contract of service or a contract for services and allowing a person to work as a volunteer; and references to an employee or to a person being employed shall be construed accordingly.

Excepted establishments

3. - (1) For the purposes of the Act, an establishment is excepted from being a care home if -

(a) it is a health service hospital at which nursing is provided;

(b) it provides accommodation, together with nursing, and is vested -

(i) in the Secretary of State for the purposes of his functions under the National Health Service Act 1977[7]; or

(ii) in an NHS trust[8];

(c) it is a university;

(d) it is an institution within the further education sector as defined by section 91(3) of the Further and Higher Education Act 1992[9]; or

(e) it is a school.

(2) For the purposes of paragraph (1), "university" includes -

(a) any university college;

(b) any college, or institution in the nature of a college, of a university.

(3) The exception in paragraph (1)(d) does not apply if -

(a) the establishment provides accommodation together with nursing or personal care to any person; and

(b) the number of such persons is more than one tenth of the number of students to whom it provides both education and accommodation.

Statement of purpose

4. - (1) The registered person shall compile in relation to the care home a written statement (in these Regulations referred to as "the statement of purpose") which shall consist of -

(a) a statement of the aims and objectives of the care home;

(b) a statement as to the facilities and services which are to be provided by the registered person for service users; and

(c) a statement as to the matters listed in Schedule 1.

(2) The registered person shall supply a copy of the statement of purpose to the Commission and shall make a copy of it available on request for inspection by every service user and any representative of a service user.

(3) Nothing in regulation 16(1) or 23(1) shall require or authorise the registered person to contravene, or not to comply with -

(a) any other provision of these Regulations; or

(b) the conditions for the time being in force in relation to the registration of the registered person under Part II of the Act.

Service user's guide

5. - (1) The registered person shall produce a written guide to the care home (in these Regulations referred to as "the service user's guide") which shall include -

(a) a summary of the statement of purpose;

(b) the terms and conditions in respect of accommodation to be provided for service users, including as to the amount and method of payment of fees;

(c) a standard form of contract for the provision of services and facilities by the registered provider to service users;

(d) the most recent inspection report;

(e) a summary of the complaints procedure established under regulation 22;

(f) the address and telephone number of the Commission.

(2) The registered person shall supply a copy of the service user's guide to the Commission and each service user.

(3) Where a local authority has made arrangements for the provision of accommodation, nursing or personal care to the service user at the care home, the registered person shall supply to the service user a copy of the agreement specifying the arrangements made.

Review of statement of purpose and service user's guide

6. The registered person shall -

(a) keep under review and, where appropriate, revise the statement of purpose and the service user's guide; and

(b) notify the Commission and service users of any such revision within 28 days.

PART II

REGISTERED PERSONS

Fitness of registered provider

7. - (1) A person shall not carry on a care home unless he is fit to do so.

(2) A person is not fit to carry on a care home unless the person -

(a) is an individual who carries on the care home -

  (i) otherwise than in partnership with others, and he satisfies the requirements set out in paragraph (3);

  (ii) in partnership with others, and he and each of his partners satisfies the requirements set out in paragraph (3);

(b) is a partnership, and each of the partners satisfies the requirements set out in paragraph (3);

(c) is an organisation and -

  (i) the organisation has given notice to the Commission of the name, address and position in the organisation of an individual (in these Regulations referred to as "the responsible individual") who is a director, manager, secretary or other officer of the organisation and is responsible for supervising the management of the care home; and

  (ii) that individual satisfies the requirements set out in paragraph (3).

(3) The requirements are that -

(a) he is of integrity and good character; and

(b) he is physically and mentally fit to carry on the care home; and

(c) full and satisfactory information is available in relation to him in respect of the following matters -

  (i) the matters specified in paragraphs 1 to 5 and 7 of Schedule 2;

(5) A person shall not carry on a care home if -

(a) he has been adjudged bankrupt or sequestration of his estate has been awarded and (in either case) he has not been discharged and the bankruptcy order has not been annulled or rescinded; or

(b) he has made a composition or arrangement with his creditors and has not been discharged in respect of it.

Appointment of manager

8. - (1) The registered provider shall appoint an individual to manage the care home where -

(a) there is no registered manager in respect of the care home; and

(b) the registered provider -

  (i) is an organisation or partnership;

  (ii) is not a fit person to manage a care home; or

(iii) is not, or does not intend to be, in full-time day to day charge of the care home.

(2) Where the registered provider appoints a person to manage the care home he shall forthwith give notice to the Commission of -

(a) the name of the person so appointed; and

(b) the date on which the appointment is to take effect.

Fitness of registered manager

9. - (1) A person shall not manage a care home unless he is fit to do so.

(2) A person is not fit to manage a care home unless -

(a) he is of integrity and good character;

(b) having regard to the size of the care home, the statement of purpose, and the number and needs of the service users -

(i) he has the qualifications, skills and experience necessary for managing the care home; and

(ii) he is physically and mentally fit to manage the care home; and

(c) full and satisfactory information is available in relation to him in respect of the following matters -

(i) the matters specified in paragraphs 1 to 5 and 7 of Schedule 2;

Registered person: general requirements

10. - (1) The registered provider and the registered manager shall, having regard to the size of the care home, the statement of purpose, and the number and needs of the service users, carry on or manage the care home (as the case may be) with sufficient care, competence and skill.

(2) If the registered provider is -

(a) an individual, he shall undertake;

(b) an organisation, it shall ensure that the responsible individual undertakes;

(c) a partnership, it shall ensure that one of the partners undertakes,

from time to time such training as is appropriate to ensure that he has the experience and skills necessary for carrying on the care home.

(3) The registered manager shall undertake from time to time such training as is appropriate to ensure that he has the experience and skills necessary for managing the care home.

Notification of offences

11. Where the registered person or the responsible individual is convicted of any criminal offence, whether in England and Wales or elsewhere, he shall forthwith give notice in writing to the Commission of -

(a) the date and place of the conviction;

(b) the offence of which he was convicted; and

(c) the penalty imposed on him in respect of the offence.

PART III

CONDUCT OF CARE HOME

Health and welfare of service users

12. - (1) The registered person shall ensure that the care home is conducted so as -

(a) to promote and make proper provision for the health and welfare of service users;

(b) to make proper provision for the care and, where appropriate, treatment, education and supervision of service users.

(2) The registered person shall so far as practicable enable service users to make decisions with respect to the care they are to receive and their health and welfare.

(3) The registered person shall, for the purpose of providing care to service users, and making proper provision for their health and welfare, so far as practicable ascertain and take into account their wishes and feelings.

(4) The registered person shall make suitable arrangements to ensure that the care home is conducted -

(a) in a manner which respects the privacy and dignity of service users;

(b) with due regard to the sex, religious persuasion, racial origin, and cultural and linguistic background and any disability of service users.

(5) The registered provider and registered manager (if any) shall, in relation to the conduct of the care home -

(a) maintain good personal and professional relationships with each other and with service users and staff; and

(b) encourage and assist staff to maintain good personal and professional relationships with service users.

Further requirements as to health and welfare

13. - (1) The registered person shall make arrangements for service users -

(a) to be registered with a general practitioner of their choice; and

(b) to receive where necessary, treatment, advice and other services from any health care professional.

(2) The registered person shall make arrangements for the recording, handling, safekeeping, safe administration and disposal of medicines received into the care home.

(3) The registered person shall make suitable arrangements to prevent infection, toxic conditions and the spread of infection at the care home.

(4) The registered person shall ensure that -

(a) all parts of the home to which service users have access are so far as reasonably practicable free from hazards to their safety;

(b) any activities in which service users participate are so far as reasonably practicable free from avoidable risks; and

(c) unnecessary risks to the health or safety of service users are identified and so far as possible eliminated,

and shall make suitable arrangements for the training of staff in first aid.

(5) The registered person shall make suitable arrangements to provide a safe system for moving and handling service users.

(6) The registered person shall make arrangements, by training staff or by other measures, to prevent service users being harmed or suffering abuse or being placed at risk of harm or abuse.

(7) The registered person shall ensure that no service user is subject to physical restraint unless restraint of the kind employed is the only practicable means of securing the welfare of that or any other service user and there are exceptional circumstances.

(8) On any occasion on which a service user is subject to physical restraint, the registered person shall record the circumstances, including the nature of the restraint.

Assessment of service users

14. - (1) The registered person shall not provide accommodation to a service user at the care home unless, so far as it shall have been practicable to do so -

(a) needs of the service user have been assessed by a suitably qualified or suitably trained person;

(b) the registered person has obtained a copy of the assessment;

(c) there has been appropriate consultation regarding the assessment with the service user or a representative of the service user;

(d) the registered person has confirmed in writing to the service user that having regard to the assessment the care home is suitable for the purpose of meeting the service user's needs in respect of his health and welfare.

(2) The registered person shall ensure that the assessment of the service user's needs is -

(a) kept under review; and

(b) revised at any time when it is necessary to do so having regard to any change of circumstances.

Service user's plan

15. - (1) Unless it is impracticable to carry out such consultation, the registered person shall, after consultation with the service user, or a representative of his, prepare a written plan ("the service user's plan") as to how the service user's needs in respect of his health and welfare are to be met.

(2) The registered person shall -

(a) make the service user's plan available to the service user;

(b) keep the service user's plan under review;

(c) where appropriate and, unless it is impracticable to carry out such consultation, after consultation with the service user or a representative of his, revise the service user's plan; and

(d) notify the service user of any such revision.

Facilities and services

16. - (1) Subject to regulation 4(3), the registered person shall provide facilities and services to service users in accordance with the statement required by regulation 4(1)(b) in respect of the care home.

(2) The registered person shall having regard to the size of the care home and the number and needs of service users -

(a) provide, so far as is necessary for the purpose of managing the care home -

(i) appropriate telephone facilities;

(ii) appropriate facilities for communication by facsimile transmission;

(b) provide telephone facilities which are suitable for the needs of service users, and make arrangements to enable service users to use such facilities in private;

(c) provide in rooms occupied by service users adequate furniture, bedding and other furnishings, including curtains and floor coverings, and equipment suitable to the needs of service users and screens where necessary;

(d) permit service users, so far as it is practicable to do so, to bring their own furniture and furnishings into the rooms they occupy;

(e) arrange for the regular laundering of linen and clothing;

(f) so far as it is practicable to do so, provide adequate facilities for service users to wash, dry and iron their own clothes if they so wish and, for that purpose, to make arrangements for their clothes to be sorted and kept separately;

(g) provide sufficient and suitable kitchen equipment, crockery, cutlery and utensils, and adequate facilities for the preparation and storage of food;

(h) provide adequate facilities for service users to prepare their own food and ensure that such facilities are safe for use by service users;

(i) provide, in adequate quantities, suitable, wholesome and nutritious food which is varied and properly prepared and available at such time as may reasonably be required by service users;

(j) after consultation with the environmental health authority, make suitable arrangements for maintaining satisfactory standards of hygiene in the care home;

(k) keep the care home free from offensive odours and make suitable arrangements for the disposal of general and clinical waste;

(l) provide a place where the money and valuables of service users may be deposited for safe keeping, and make arrangements for service users to acknowledge in writing the return to them of any money or valuables so deposited;

(m) consult service users about their social interests, and make arrangements to enable them to engage in local, social and community activities and to visit, or maintain contact or communicate with, their families and friends;

(n) consult service users about the programme of activities arranged by or on behalf of the care home, and provide facilities for recreation including, having regard to the needs of service users, activities in relation to recreation, fitness and training.

(3) The registered person shall ensure that so far as practicable service users have the opportunity to attend religious services of their choice.

(4) In this regulation "food" includes drink.

Records

17. - (1) The registered person shall -

(a) maintain in respect of each service user a record which includes the information, documents and other records specified in Schedule 3 relating to the service user;

(b) ensure that the record referred to in sub-paragraph (a) is kept securely in the care home.

(2) The registered person shall maintain in the care home the records specified in Schedule 4.

(3) The registered person shall ensure that the records referred to in paragraphs (1) and (2) -

(a) are kept up to date; and

(b) are at all times available for inspection in the care home by any person authorised by the Commission to enter and inspect the care home.

(4) The records referred to in paragraphs (1) and (2) shall be retained for not less than three years from the date of the last entry.

Staffing

18. - (1) The registered person shall, having regard to the size of the care home, the statement of purpose and the number and needs of service users -

(a) ensure that at all times suitably qualified, competent and experienced persons are working at the care home in such numbers as are appropriate for the health and welfare of service users;

(b) ensure that the employment of any persons on a temporary basis at the care home will not prevent service users from receiving such continuity of care as is reasonable to meet their needs;

(c) ensure that the persons employed by the registered person to work at the care home receive -

(i) training appropriate to the work they are to perform; and

(ii) suitable assistance, including time off, for the purpose of obtaining further qualifications appropriate to such work.

(2) The registered person shall ensure that persons working at the care home are appropriately supervised.

(3) Where the care home -

(a) provides nursing to service users; and

(b) provides, whether or not in connection with nursing, medicines or medical treatment to service users,

the registered person shall ensure that at all times a suitably qualified registered nurse is working at the care home.

(4) The registered person shall make arrangements for providing persons who work at the care home with appropriate information about any code of practice published under section 62 of the

Act.

Fitness of workers

19. - (1) The registered person shall not employ a person to work at the care home unless -

(a) the person is fit to work at the care home;

(b) subject to paragraph (6), he has obtained in respect of that person the information and documents specified in -

(i) paragraphs 1 to 7 of Schedule 2;

(c) he is satisfied on reasonable grounds as to the authenticity of the references referred to in paragraph 5 of Schedule 2 in respect of that person.

(2) This paragraph applies to a person who is employed by a person ("the employer") other than the registered person.

(3) This paragraph applies to a position in which a person may in the course of his duties have regular contact with service users at the care home or with any other person of a description specified in section 3(2) of the Act.

(4) The registered person shall not allow a person to whom paragraph (2) applies to work at the care home in a position to which paragraph (3) applies, unless -

(a) the person is fit to work at the care home;

(b) the employer has obtained in respect of that person the information and documents specified in -

(i) paragraphs 1 to 7 of Schedule 2;

and has confirmed in writing to the registered person that he has done so; and

(c) the employer is satisfied on reasonable grounds as to the authenticity of the references referred to in paragraph 5 of Schedule 2 in respect of that person, and has confirmed in writing to the registered person that he is so satisfied.

(5) For the purposes of paragraphs (1) and (4), a person is not fit to work at a care home unless -

(a) he is of integrity and good character;

(b) he has qualifications suitable to the work that he is to perform, and the skills and experience necessary for such work;

(c) he is physically and mentally fit for the purposes of the work which he is to perform at the care home; and

(d) full and satisfactory information is available in relation to him in respect of the following matters -

(i) each of the matters specified in paragraphs 1 to 6 of Schedule 2;

(ii) except where paragraph (7) applies, each of the matters specified in paragraph 7 of that Schedule;

(iii) where paragraph (7) applies, each of the matters specified in paragraph 8 of that Schedule.

(6) Paragraphs (1)(b) and (5)(d), in so far as they relate to paragraph 7 of Schedule 2, shall not apply until 1st April 2003 in respect of a person who immediately before 1st April 2002 is employed to work at the care home.

Restrictions on acting for service user

20. - (1) Subject to paragraph (2), the registered person shall not pay money belonging to any service user into a bank account unless -

(a) the account is in the name of the service user, or any of the service users, to which the money belongs; and

(b) the account is not used by the registered person in connection with the carrying on or management of the care home.

(2) Paragraph (1) does not apply to money which is paid to the registered person in respect of charges payable by a service user for accommodation or other services provided by the registered person at the care home.

(3) The registered person shall ensure so far as practicable that persons working at the care home do not act as the agent of a service user.

Staff views as to conduct of care home

21. - (1) This regulation applies to any matter relating to the conduct of the care home so far as it may affect the health or welfare of service users.

(2) The registered person shall make arrangements to enable staff to inform the registered person and the Commission of their views about any matter to which this regulation applies.

Complaints

22. - (1) The registered person shall establish a procedure ("the complaints procedure") for considering complaints made to the registered person by a service user or person acting on the service user's behalf.

(2) The complaints procedure shall be appropriate to the needs of service users.

(3) The registered person shall ensure that any complaint made under the complaints procedure is fully investigated.

(4) The registered person shall, within 28 days after the date on which the complaint is made, or such shorter period as may be reasonable in the circumstances, inform the person who made the complaint of the action (if any) that is to be taken.

(5) The registered person shall supply a written copy of the complaints procedure to every service user and to any person acting on behalf of a service user if that person so requests.

(6) Where a written copy of the complaints procedure is to be supplied in accordance with paragraph (5) to a person who is blind or whose vision is impaired, the registered person shall so far as it is practicable to do so supply, in addition to the written copy, a copy of the complaints procedure in a form which is suitable for that person.

(7) The copy of the complaints procedure to be supplied in accordance with paragraphs (5) and (6) shall include -

   (a) the name, address and telephone number of the Commission; and

   (b) the procedure (if any) that has been notified by the Commission to the registered person for the making of complaints to the Commission relating to the care home.

(8) The registered person shall supply to the Commission at its request a statement containing a summary of the complaints made during the preceding twelve months and the action that was taken in response.

PART IV

PREMISES

Fitness of premises

23. - (1) Subject to regulation 4(3), the registered person shall not use premises for the purposes of a care home unless -

   (a) the premises are suitable for the purpose of achieving the aims and objectives set out in the statement of purpose; and

   (b) the location of the premises is appropriate to the needs of service users.

(2) The registered person shall having regard to the number and needs of the service users ensure that -

   (a) the physical design and layout of the premises to be used as the care home meet the needs of the service users;

   (b) the premises to be used as the care home are of sound construction and kept in a good state of repair externally and internally;

   (c) equipment provided at the care home for use by service users or persons who work at the care home is maintained in good working order;

(d) all parts of the care home are kept clean and reasonably decorated;

(e) adequate private and communal accommodation is provided for service users;

(f) the size and layout of rooms occupied or used by service users are suitable for their needs;

(g) there is adequate sitting, recreational and dining space provided separately from the service user's private accommodation;

(h) the communal space provided for service users is suitable for the provision of social, cultural and religious activities appropriate to the circumstances of service users;

(i) suitable facilities are provided for service users to meet visitors in communal accommodation, and in private accommodation which is separate from the service users' own private rooms;

(j) there are provided at appropriate places in the premises sufficient numbers of lavatories, and of wash-basins, baths and showers fitted with a hot and cold water supply;

(k) any necessary sluicing facilities are provided;

(l) suitable provision is made for storage for the purposes of the care home;

(m) suitable storage facilities are provided for the use of service users;

(n) suitable adaptations are made, and such support, equipment and facilities, including passenger lifts, as may be required are provided, for service users who are old, infirm or physically disabled;

(o) external grounds which are suitable for, and safe for use by, service users are provided and appropriately maintained;

(p) ventilation, heating and lighting suitable for service users is provided in all parts of the care home which are used by service users.

(3) The registered person shall provide for staff -

(a) suitable facilities and accommodation, other than sleeping accommodation, including -

(i) facilities for the purpose of changing;

(ii) storage facilities;

(b) sleeping accommodation where the provision of such accommodation is needed by staff in connection with their work at the care home.

(4) The registered person shall after consultation with the fire authority -

(a) take adequate precautions against the risk of fire, including the provision of suitable fire equipment;

(b) provide adequate means of escape;

(c) make adequate arrangements -

    (i) for detecting, containing and extinguishing fires;

    (ii) for giving warnings of fires;

    (iii) for the evacuation, in the event of fire, of all persons in the care home and safe placement of service users;

    (iv) for the maintenance of all fire equipment; and

    (v) for reviewing fire precautions, and testing fire equipment, at suitable intervals;

(d) make arrangements for persons working at the care home to receive suitable training in fire prevention; and

(e) to ensure, by means of fire drills and practices at suitable intervals, that the persons working at the care home and, so far as practicable, service users, are aware of the procedure to be followed in case of fire, including the procedure for saving life.

(5) The registered person shall undertake appropriate consultation with the authority responsible for environmental health for the area in which the care home is situated.

PART V

MANAGEMENT

Review of quality of care

24. - (1) The registered person shall establish and maintain a system for -

(a) reviewing at appropriate intervals; and

(b) improving,

the quality of care provided at the care home, including the quality of nursing where nursing is provided at the care home.

(2) The registered person shall supply to the Commission a report in respect of any review conducted by him for the purposes of paragraph (1), and make a copy of the report available to service users.

(3) The system referred to in paragraph (1) shall provide for consultation with service users and their representatives.

Financial position

25. - (1) The registered provider shall carry on the care home in such manner as is likely to ensure that the care home will be financially viable for the purpose of achieving the aims and objectives set out in the statement of purpose.

(2) The registered person shall, if the Commission so requests, provide the Commission with such information and documents as it may require for the purpose of considering the financial viability of the care home, including -

  (a) the annual accounts of the care home certified by an accountant;

  (b) a reference from a bank expressing an opinion as to the registered provider's financial standing;

  (c) information as to the financing and financial resources of the care home;

  (d) where the registered provider is a company, information as to any of its associated companies;

  (e) a certificate of insurance for the registered provider in respect of liability which may be incurred by him in relation to the care home in respect of death, injury, public liability, damage or other loss.

(3) The registered person shall -

  (a) ensure that adequate accounts are maintained in respect of the care home and kept up to date;

  (b) ensure that the accounts give details of the running costs of the care home, including rent, payments under a mortgage and expenditure on food, heating and salaries and wages of staff; and

  (c) supply a copy of the accounts to the Commission at its request.

(4) In this regulation a company is an associated company of another if one of them has control of the other or both are under the control of the same person.

Visits by registered provider

26. - (1) Where the registered provider is an individual, but not in day to day charge of the care home, he shall visit the care home in accordance with this regulation.

(2) Where the registered provider is an organisation or partnership, the care home shall be visited in accordance with this regulation by -

  (a) the responsible individual or one of the partners, as the case may be;

  (b) another of the directors or other persons responsible for the management of the organisation or partnership; or

  (c) an employee of the organisation or the partnership who is not directly concerned with the conduct of the care home.

(3) Visits under paragraph (1) or (2) shall take place at least once a month and shall be unannounced.

(4) The person carrying out the visit shall -

(a) interview, with their consent and in private, such of the service users and their representatives and persons working at the care home as appears necessary in order to form an opinion of the standard of care provided in the care home;

(b) inspect the premises of the care home, its record of events and records of any complaints; and

(c) prepare a written report on the conduct of the care home.

(5) The registered provider shall supply a copy of the report required to be made under paragraph (4)(c) to -

(a) the Commission;

(b) the registered manager; and

(c) in the case of a visit under paragraph (2) -

(i) where the registered provider is an organisation, to each of the directors or other persons responsible for the management of the organisation; and

(ii) where the registered provider is a partnership, to each of the partners.

PART VI

CHILDREN

Application of this Part

27. The provisions of this Part shall apply where any child is accommodated in the care home.

Interpretation

28. In regulation 2, paragraph (1) shall have effect as if -

(a) at the end of the definition of "service user" there were added the words ", or any child who is accommodated in the care home";

(b) the following definitions were added at the appropriate places -

" "placement plan" has the meaning given to it in regulation 12 (child's placement plan) of the Children's Homes Regulations 2001[10];

"placing authority" has the meaning given to it in regulation 2(1) (interpretation) of the Children's Homes Regulations 2001;".

Statement of purpose

29. In regulation 4, paragraph (1) shall have effect as if at the end of that paragraph there were added the following -

" and
(d) the information specified in Schedule 5.".

Registered person

30. - (1) In regulation 7, paragraph (3) shall have effect as if at the end of that paragraph there were added the following -

> " and
> (d) his skills and experience are suitable for the purpose of his working with children.".

(2) In regulation 9, paragraph (2) shall have effect as if at the end of that paragraph there were added the following -

> " and
> (d) his skills and experience are suitable for the purpose of his working with children and either -
>
> > (i) his qualifications are suitable for the purpose of his working with children; or
> >
> > (ii) another person has been appointed for the purpose of assisting him in the management of the care home, and the qualifications of the person so appointed are suitable for the purpose of his working with children.".

(3) In regulation 10, paragraph (1) shall have effect as if for the words "and the number and needs of the service users," there were substituted the words "the number and needs of the service users and the need to safeguard and promote the welfare of children accommodated in the care home,".

Separate provision for children

31. - (1) Subject to paragraph (2), the registered person shall ensure that -

(a) the provision to be made for the care, treatment and supervision of children accommodated in the care home; and

(b) the provision of facilities and services to them,

shall, so far as it is practicable to do so, be made separately from other service users.

(2) Paragraph (1) shall not prevent the registered person from making provision jointly for children and other service users whose age does not significantly differ from those children.

Welfare and protection of children

32. - (1) Regulation 12 of these Regulations shall have effect as if, at the end of sub-paragraph (a) of paragraph (1) of that regulation there were added the words ", including provision for safeguarding the welfare of children accommodated in the care home".

(2) The provisions of regulations 12, 15 to 18, 23 and 30 of, and Schedule 5 to, the Children's Homes Regulations 2001 (child's placement plan; contact and access to communications; arrangements for the protection of children; behaviour management, discipline and restraint;

education, employment and leisure activity; hazards and safety; notifiable events) shall apply to the registered person as if -

(a) any reference to the registered person were to the registered person as defined in these Regulations;

(b) any reference to the children's home or the home were to the care home.

(3) Where the registered person notifies the Commission in accordance with regulation 30 of the Children's Homes Regulations 2001 of any of the following events, namely -

(a) serious illness or a serious accident sustained by a child accommodated at the care home;

(b) the outbreak of any infectious disease at the care home or involving children accommodated at the care home,

he will not be required to give separate notice of that event to the Commission under regulation 37 (notification of death, illness and other events) of these Regulations.

Fitness of workers

33. Regulation 19 shall have effect as if -

(a) in sub-paragraph (b) of paragraph (1) and sub-paragraph (b) of paragraph (4), for head (i) in each of those sub-paragraphs there were substituted the following head -

" (i) paragraphs 1 to 6 of Schedule 2 and in Schedule 6;";

(b) in sub-paragraph (d) of paragraph (5), for head (i) there were substituted the following head -

" (i) each of the matters specified in paragraphs 1 to 6 of Schedule 2 and in Schedule 6;";

(c) at the end of paragraph (5) there were added the following -

" and
(d) his qualifications, skills and experience are suitable for the purpose of working with children.".

Staff disciplinary procedure

34. The registered person shall operate a staff disciplinary procedure which, in particular -

(a) provides for the suspension of an employee of his where necessary in the interests of the safety or welfare of children accommodated in the care home; and

(b) provides that the failure on the part of an employee of his to report an incident of abuse, or suspected abuse of a child accommodated in the care home to an appropriate person is a ground on which disciplinary proceedings may be instituted.

Review of quality of care

35. Regulation 24 shall have effect as if -

(a) the system referred to in paragraph (1) of regulation 24 included monitoring at appropriate intervals the matters set out in Schedule 7;

(b) in paragraph (2) of regulation 24, after the words "any review conducted by him" there were added the words ", or any matters monitored";

(c) in paragraph (3) of regulation 24, for the words "and their representatives" there were substituted the words ", their representatives, the parents of the children accommodated at the care home and, in relation to those children, the placing authorities".

Offences

36. Regulation 43 shall have effect as if for paragraph (1) there were substituted the following paragraph -

" (1) A contravention or failure to comply with any of the following provisions shall be an offence -

(a) regulations 4, 5, 11, 12(1) to (4), 13(1) to (4) and (6) to (8), 14, 15, 16(1), (2)(a) to (j) and (l) to (n) and (3), 17 to 26 and 37 to 40, to the extent that those regulations have effect subject to Part VI of these Regulations;

(b) regulations 31 and 34; and

(c) the provisions referred to in paragraph (2) of regulation 32, to the extent that they apply to the registered person by virtue of that paragraph.".

PART VII

MISCELLANEOUS

Notification of death, illness and other events

37. - (1) The registered person shall give notice to the Commission without delay of the occurrence of -

(a) the death of any service user, including the circumstances of his death;

(b) the outbreak in the care home of any infectious disease which in the opinion of any registered medical practitioner attending persons in the care home is sufficiently serious to be so notified;

(c) any serious injury to a service user;

(d) serious illness of a service user at a care home at which nursing is not provided;

(e) any event in the care home which adversely affects the well-being or safety of any service user;

(f) any theft, burglary or accident in the care home;

(g) any allegation of misconduct by the registered person or any person who works at the care home.

(2) Any notification made in accordance with this regulation which is given orally shall be confirmed in writing.

Notice of absence

38. - (1) Where -

(a) the registered provider, if he is an individual; or

(b) the registered manager,

proposes to be absent from the care home for a continuous period of 28 days or more, the registered person shall give notice in writing to the Commission of the proposed absence.

(2) Except in the case of an emergency, the notice referred to in paragraph (1) above shall be given no later than one month before the proposed absence commences or within such shorter period as may be agreed with the Commission and the notice shall specify -

(a) the length or expected length of the absence;

(b) the reason for the absence;

(c) the arrangements which have been made for the running of the care home during that absence;

(d) the name, address and qualifications of the person who will be responsible for the care home during that absence; and

(e) in the case of the absence of the registered manager, the arrangements that have been, or are proposed to be, made for appointing another person to manage the care home during that absence, including the proposed date by which the appointment is to be made.

(3) Where the absence arises as a result of an emergency, the registered person shall give notice of the absence within one week of its occurrence specifying the matters mentioned in sub-paragraphs (a) to (e) of paragraph (2).

(4) Where -

(a) the registered provider, if he is an individual; or

(b) the registered manager,

has been absent from the care home for a continuous period of 28 days or more, and the Commission has not been given notice of the absence, the registered person shall without delay give notice in writing to the Commission of the absence, specifying the matters mentioned in sub-paragraphs (a) to (e) of paragraph (2).

(5) The registered person shall notify the Commission of the return to duty of the registered provider or (as the case may be) the registered manager not later than 7 days after the date of his return.

Notice of changes

39. The registered person shall give notice in writing to the Commission as soon as it is practicable to do so if any of the following events takes place or is proposed to take place -

(a) a person other than the registered person carries on or manages the care home;

(b) a person ceases to carry on or manage the care home;

(c) where the registered person is an individual, he changes his name;

(d) where the registered provider is a partnership, there is any change in the membership of the partnership;

(e) where the registered provider is an organisation -

(i) the name or address of the organisation is changed;

(ii) there is any change of director, manager, secretary or other similar officer of the organisation;

(iii) there is to be any change of responsible individual;

(f) where the registered provider is an individual, a trustee in bankruptcy is appointed;

(g) where the registered provider is a company or partnership, a receiver, manager, liquidator or provisional liquidator is appointed; or

(h) the premises of the care home are significantly altered or extended, or additional premises are acquired.

Notice of termination of accommodation

40. - (1) Subject to paragraph (2), the registered person shall not terminate the arrangements for the accommodation of a service user unless he has given reasonable notice of his intention to do so to -

(a) the service user;

(b) the person who appears to be the service user's next of kin; and

(c) where a local authority has made arrangements for the provision of accommodation, nursing or personal care to the service user at the care home, that authority.

(2) If it is impracticable for the registered person to comply with the requirement in paragraph (1) -

(a) he shall do so as soon as it is practicable to do so; and

(b) he shall provide to the Commission a statement as to the circumstances which made it impracticable for him to comply with the requirement.

Appointment of liquidators etc.

41. - (1) Any person to whom paragraph (2) applies must -

(a) forthwith notify the Commission of his appointment, indicating the reasons for it;

(b) appoint a manager to take full-time day to day charge of the care home in any case where there is no registered manager; and

(c) within 28 days of his appointment notify the Commission of his intentions regarding the future operation of the care home.

(2) This paragraph applies to any person appointed as -

(a) the receiver or manager of the property of a company or partnership which is a registered provider in respect of a care home;

(b) a liquidator or provisional liquidator of a company which is a registered provider of a care home; or

(c) the trustee in bankruptcy of a registered provider of a care home.

Death of registered person

42. - (1) If more than one person is registered in respect of a care home, and a registered person dies, the surviving registered person shall without delay notify the Commission of the death in writing.

(2) If only one person is registered in respect of a care home, and he dies, his personal representatives shall notify the Commission in writing -

(a) without delay of the death; and

(b) within 28 days of their intentions regarding the future running of the home.

(3) The personal representatives of the deceased registered provider may carry on the care home without being registered in respect of it -

(a) for a period not exceeding 28 days; and

(b) for any further period as may be determined in accordance with paragraph (4).

(4) The Commission may extend the period specified in paragraph (3)(a) by such further period, not exceeding one year, as the Commission shall determine, and shall notify any such determination to the personal representatives in writing.

(5) The personal representatives shall appoint a person to take full-time day to day charge of the home during any period in which, in accordance with paragraph (3), they carry on the care home without being registered in respect of it.

Offences

43. - (1) A contravention or failure to comply with any of the provisions of regulations 4, 5, 11, 12(1) to (4), 13(1) to (4) and (6) to (8), 14, 15, 16(1), (2)(a) to (j) and (1) to (n) and (3), 17 to 26 and 37 to 40, shall be an offence.

(2) The Commission shall not bring proceedings against a person in respect of any contravention or failure to comply with those regulations unless -

(a) subject to paragraph (4), he is a registered person;

(b) notice has been given to him in accordance with paragraph (3);

(c) the period specified in the notice, within which the registered person may make representations to the Commission, has expired; and

(d) in a case where, in accordance with paragraph (3)(b), the notice specifies any action that is to be taken within a specified period, the period has expired and the action has not been taken within that period.

(3) Where the Commission considers that the registered person has contravened or failed to comply with any of the provisions of the regulations mentioned in paragraph (1), it may serve a notice on the registered person specifying -

(a) in what respect in its opinion the registered person has contravened or is contravening any of the regulations, or has failed or is failing to comply with the requirements of any of the regulations;

(b) where it is practicable for the registered person to take action for the purpose of complying with any of those regulations, the action which, in the opinion of the Commission, the registered person should take for that purpose;

(c) the period, not exceeding three months, within which the registered person should take any action specified in accordance with sub-paragraph (b);

(d) the period, not exceeding one month, within which the registered person may make representations to the Commission about the notice.

(4) The Commission may bring proceedings against a person who was once, but no longer is, a registered person, in respect of a failure to comply with regulation 17 and for this purpose, references in paragraphs (2) and (3) to a registered person shall be taken to include such a

person.

Compliance with regulations

44. Where there is more than one registered person in respect of a care home, anything which is required under these regulations to be done by the registered person shall, if done by one of the registered persons, not be required to be done by any of the other registered persons.

Adult placements

45. - (1) For the purposes of this regulation and regulation 46, a registered provider is an adult placement carer in respect of a care home if -

(a) he is the registered provider in respect of, and manages, the care home;

(b) no person other than the registered provider manages the care home;

(c) the care home is, or forms part of -

(i) the registered provider's home; or

(ii) if the registered provider has more than one home, the home where he ordinarily resides;

(d) no more than three service users are accommodated in the care home;

(e) a placement agreement has been made in respect of each of the service users;

(f) each service user is over the age of 18.

(2) In this regulation, "placement agreement" means an agreement that -

(a) has been made between -

(i) the registered provider;

(ii) the service user;

(iii) the local authority or other body which manages a scheme ("adult placement scheme") under which it has arranged or proposes to arrange for the service user to be accommodated in a care home;

(b) makes provision for the following matters -

(i) the aims of the arrangements under which the service user is accommodated in the care home;

(ii) the room to be occupied by the service user;

(iii) the services to be provided to the service user;

(iv) the fees to be charged;

(v) the qualifications and experience of the registered provider;

(vi) the terms and conditions in respect of the accommodation and services to be provided;

(vii) services and assistance to be provided under the adult placement scheme under which the accommodation is or has been arranged.

Modification of regulations in respect of adult placement carers

46. - (1) The following provisions of this regulation shall apply where the registered provider is an adult placement carer in respect of a care home.

(2) Regulations 4, 8, 18, 19, 21, 24, 26 to 36 and 41 (statement of purpose; appointment of manager; staffing; fitness of workers; staff views as to conduct of care home; review of quality of care home; visits by registered provider; children; appointment of liquidators etc.) and Schedules 1 and 5 to 7 (information to be included in the statement of purpose; additional information to be included in the statement of purpose where children are accommodated; additional information and documents to be obtained in respect of persons working at a care home where children are accommodated; and matters to be monitored at a care home where children are accommodated) shall not apply.

(3) Regulation 5 (service user's guide) shall have effect as if sub-paragraph (a) of paragraph (1) of that regulation were omitted.

(4) Regulation 6 (review of statement of purpose and service user's guide) shall have effect as if in paragraph (a) of that regulation the words "the statement of purpose and" were omitted.

(5) Regulation 16 (facilities and services) shall have effect as if in sub-paragraph (j) of paragraph (2) of that regulation the words "after consultation with the environmental health authority" were omitted.

(6) Regulation 23 (fitness of premises) shall have effect as if sub-paragraphs (a), (f), (g), (h), (j), (k) and (n) of paragraph (2) and paragraphs (3) to (5) of that regulation were omitted.

(7) Regulation 25 (financial position) shall have effect as if -

(a) paragraph (1) of that regulation were omitted;

(b) in paragraph (2) of that regulation, sub-paragraphs (a) to (d) were omitted;

(c) paragraphs (3) and (4) of that regulation were omitted.

(8) Schedule 3 (records to be kept in a care home in respect of each service user) shall have effect as if sub-paragraph (j) of paragraph 3 of that Schedule were omitted.

(9) Schedule 4 (other records to be kept in a care home) shall have effect as if paragraphs 1, 3, 5, 6, 7 and 12 to 16 of that Schedule were omitted.

Signed by authority of the Secretary of State for Health

Jacqui Smith
Minister of State, Department of Health

11th December 2001

SCHEDULE 1

INFORMATION TO BE INCLUDED IN THE STATEMENT OF PURPOSE

1. The name and address of the registered provider and of any registered manager.

2. The relevant qualifications and experience of the registered provider and any registered manager.

3. The number, relevant qualifications and experience of the staff working at the care home.

4. The organisational structure of the care home.

5. The age-range and sex of the service users for whom it is intended that accommodation should be provided.

6. The range of needs that the care home is intended to meet.

7. Whether nursing is to be provided.

8. Any criteria used for admission to the care home, including the care home's policy and procedures (if any) for emergency admissions.

9. The arrangements for service users to engage in social activities, hobbies and leisure interests.

10. The arrangements made for consultation with service users about the operation of the care home.

11. The fire precautions and associated emergency procedures in the care home.

12. The arrangements made for service users to attend religious services of their choice.

13. The arrangements made for contact between service users and their relatives, friends and representatives.

14. The arrangements made for dealing with complaints.

15. The arrangements made for dealing with reviews of the service user's plan referred to in regulation 15(1).

16. The number and size of rooms in the care home.

17. Details of any specific therapeutic techniques used in the care home and arrangements made for their supervision.

18. The arrangements made for respecting the privacy and dignity of service users.

INFORMATION AND DOCUMENTS IN RESPECT OF PERSONS CARRYING ON, MANAGING OR WORKING AT A CARE HOME

1. Proof of the person's identity, including a recent photograph.

2. The person's birth certificate.

3. The person's current passport (if any).

4. Documentary evidence of any relevant qualifications of the person.

5. Two written references relating to the person.

6. Evidence that the person is physically and mentally fit for the purposes of the work which he is to perform at the care home or, where it is impracticable for the person to obtain such evidence, a declaration signed by the person that he is so fit.

7. Either -

(a) where the certificate is required for a purpose relating to section 115(5)(ea) of the Police Act 1997 (registration under Part II of the Care Standards Act 2000)[11], or the position falls within section 115(3) or (4) of that Act[12], an enhanced criminal record certificate issued under section 115 of that Act; or

(b) in any other case, a criminal record certificate issued under section 113 of that Act,

including, where applicable, the matters specified in section 113(3A) and 115(6A) of that Act and the following provisions once they are in force, namely section 113(3C)(a) and (b) and section 115(6B)(a) and (b) of that Act[13].

RECORDS TO BE KEPT IN A CARE HOME IN RESPECT OF EACH SERVICE USER

1. The following documents in respect of each service user -

(a) the assessment referred to in regulation 14(1);

(b) the service user's plan referred to in regulation 15(1).

2. A photograph of the service user.

3. A record of the following matters in respect of each service user -

(a) the name, address, date of birth and marital status of each service user;

(b) the name, address and telephone number of the service user's next of kin or of any person authorised to act on his behalf;

(c) the name, address and telephone number of the service user's general practitioner and of any officer of a local social services authority whose duty it is to supervise the welfare of the service user;

(d) the date on which the service user entered the care home;

(e) the date on which the service user left the care home;

(f) if the service user is transferred to another care home or to a hospital, the name of the care home or hospital and the date on which the service user is transferred;

(g) if the service user died at the care home, the date, time and cause of death;

(h) the name and address of any authority, organisation or other body, which arranged the service user's admission to the care home;

(i) a record of all medicines kept in the care home for the service user, and the date on which they were administered to the service user;

(j) a record of any accident affecting the service user in the care home and of any other incident in the care home which is detrimental to the health or welfare of the service user, which record shall include the nature, date and time of the accident or incident, whether medical treatment was required and the name of the persons who were respectively in charge of the care home and supervising the service user;

(k) a record of any nursing provided to the service user, including a record of his condition and any treatment or surgical intervention;

(l) details of any specialist communications needs of the service user and methods of communication that may be appropriate to the service user;

(m) details of any plan relating to the service user in respect of medication, nursing, specialist health care or nutrition;

(n) a record of incidence of pressure sores and of treatment provided to the service user;

(o) a record of falls and of treatment provided to the service user;

(p) a record of any physical restraint used on the service user;

(q) a record of any limitations agreed with the service user as to the service user's freedom of choice, liberty of movement and power to make decisions.

4. A copy of correspondence relating to each service user.

SCHEDULE 4

OTHER RECORDS TO BE KEPT IN A CARE HOME

1. A copy of the statement of purpose.

2. A copy of the service user's guide.

3. A record of all accounts kept in the care home.

4. A copy of all inspection reports.

5. A copy of any report made under regulation 26(4)(c).

6. A record of all persons employed at the care home, including in respect of each person so employed -

(a) his full name, address, date of birth, qualifications and experience;

(b) a copy of his birth certificate and passport;

(c) a copy of each reference obtained in respect of him;

(d) the dates on which he commences and ceases to be so employed;

(e) the position he holds at the care home, the work that he performs and the number of hours for which he is employed each week;

(f) correspondence, reports, records of disciplinary action and any other records in relation to his employment.

7. A copy of the duty roster of persons working at the care home, and a record of whether the roster was actually worked.

8. A record of the care home's charges to service users, including any extra amounts payable for additional services not covered by those charges, and the amounts paid by or in respect of each service user.

9. A record of all money or other valuables deposited by a service user for safekeeping or received on the service user's behalf, which -

(a) shall state the date on which the money or valuables were deposited or received, the date on which any money or valuables were returned to a service user or used, at the request of the service user, on his behalf and, where applicable, the purpose for which the money or valuables were used; and

(b) shall include the written acknowledgement of the return of the money or valuables.

10. A record of furniture brought by a service user into the room occupied by him.

11. A record of all complaints made by service users or representatives or relatives of service users or by persons working at the care home about the operation of the care home, and the action taken by the registered person in respect of any such complaint.

12. A record of any of the following events that occur in the care home -

(a) any accident;

(b) any incident which is detrimental to the health or welfare of a service user, including the outbreak of infectious disease in the care home;

(c) any injury or illness;

(d) any fire;

(e) except where a record to which paragraph 14 refers is to be made, any occasion on which the fire alarm equipment is operated;

(f) any theft or burglary.

13. Records of the food provided for service users in sufficient detail to enable any person inspecting the record to determine whether the diet is satisfactory, in relation to nutrition and otherwise, and of any special diets prepared for individual service users.

14. A record of every fire practice, drill or test of fire equipment (including fire alarm equipment) conducted in the care home and of any action taken to remedy defects in the fire equipment.

15. A statement of the procedure to be followed in the event of a fire, or where a fire alarm is given.

16. A statement of the procedure to be followed in the event of accidents or in the event of a service user becoming missing.

17. A record of all visitors to the care home, including the names of visitors.

ADDITIONAL INFORMATION TO BE INCLUDED IN THE STATEMENT OF PURPOSE WHERE CHILDREN ARE ACCOMMODATED

1. The following details about the children for whom it is intended that accommodation should be provided -

(a) their age-range;

(b) their sex;

(c) the number of children;

(d) whether they are disabled, have special needs or any other special characteristics; and

(e) the range of needs that the care home is intended to meet.

2. Any criteria used for admission to the care home, including the care home's policy and procedures for emergency admissions, if applicable.

3. If the care home provides or is intended to provide accommodation for more than six children, a description of the positive outcomes intended for children in a care home of such a size, and of the care home's strategy for counteracting any adverse effects arising from its size, on the children accommodated there.

4. A description of the care home's underlying ethos and philosophy, and where this is based on any theoretical or therapeutic model, a description of that model.

5. The facilities and services to be provided or made available, within and outside the care home, for the children accommodated there.

6. The arrangements made to protect and promote the health of the children accommodated there.

7. The arrangements for the promotion of the education of the children accommodated there, including the facilities for private study.

8. The arrangements to promote children's participation in hobbies and recreational, sporting and cultural activities.

9. The arrangements made for consultation with the children accommodated there about the operation of the care home.

10. The policy on behaviour management and the use of restraint in the care home, including in particular the methods of control and discipline and the disciplinary measures which may be used, the circumstances in which any such measures will be used and who will be permitted to use and authorise them.

11. The arrangements for child protection and to counter bullying.

12. The fire precautions and associated emergency procedures in the care home.

13. The arrangements made for the children's religious instruction and observance.

14. The arrangements made for contact between a child accommodated there and his parents, relatives and friends.

15. The procedure for dealing with any unauthorised absence of a child from the care home.

16. The arrangements for dealing with complaints.

17. The arrangements for dealing with reviews of the placement plans of children accommodated there.

18. The type of accommodation and sleeping arrangements provided, and, where applicable, how children are to be grouped, and in what circumstances they are to share bedrooms.

19. Details of any specific therapeutic techniques used in the care home and arrangements for their supervision.

20. A description of the care home's policy on anti-discriminatory practice in relation to children and children's rights.

SCHEDULE 6

Regulations 19 and 33(b)

ADDITIONAL INFORMATION AND DOCUMENTS TO BE OBTAINED IN RESPECT OF PERSONS WORKING AT A CARE HOME WHERE CHILDREN ARE ACCOMMODATED

1. Two written references, including a reference from the last employer.

2. Where a person has previously worked in a position whose duties involved work with children or vulnerable adults, so far as reasonably practicable, verification of the reason why the employment or position ended.

3. A full employment history, together with a satisfactory written explanation of any gaps in employment.

SCHEDULE 7

MATTERS TO BE MONITORED AT A CARE HOME WHERE CHILDREN ARE ACCOMMODATED

1. Compliance with any plan for the care of the child prepared by the placing authority and the placement plan of each child accommodated in the care home.

2. The deposit and issue of money and other valuables handed in for safekeeping.

3. Daily menus.

4. All accidents and injuries sustained in the care home or by children accommodated there.

5. Any illnesses of children accommodated in the care home.

6. Complaints in relation to children accommodated in the care home and their outcomes.

7. Any allegations or suspicions of abuse in respect of children accommodated in the care home and the outcome of any investigation.

8. Staff recruitment records and conduct of required checks for new workers in the care home.

9. Visitors to the care home and to children in the care home.

10. Notifications of the events listed in Schedule 5 to the Children's Homes Regulations 2001.

11. Any unauthorised absence from the care home of a child accommodated there.

12. The use of disciplinary measures in respect of children accommodated in the care home.

13. The use of physical restraint in respect of children accommodated in the care home.

EXPLANATORY NOTE

(This note is not part of the Regulations)

These Regulations are made under the Care Standards Act 2000 ("the Act") and apply to England only. Part I of the Act establishes, in relation to England, the National Care Standards Commission ("the Commission") and Part II provides for the registration and inspection of establishments and agencies, including care homes, by the Commission. It also provides powers for regulations governing the conduct of establishments and agencies. The majority of Parts I and II of the Act (in so far as not already in force) will be brought into force on 1 April 2002.

These new arrangements replace the regulatory system provided for in relation to residential care homes and nursing homes by the Registered Homes Act 1984.

Regulation 3 excludes from the definition of a care home under section 3 of the Act certain NHS hospitals and establishments providing nursing, universities, schools and certain further education institutions.

Under regulations 4 and 5, each home must have a statement of purpose consisting of the matters set out in Schedule 1, and supply a guide to the home to each service user.

Regulations 7 to 10 make provision about the fitness of the persons carrying on and managing the home, and require satisfactory information to be available in relation to certain specified matters. Where an organisation carries on the home, it must nominate a responsible individual in respect of whom this information must be available (regulation 7). Regulation 8 prescribes the circumstances where a manager must be appointed for the home, and regulation 10 imposes general requirements in relation to the proper conduct of the home, and the need for appropriate training.

Part III makes provision about the conduct of care homes, in particular as to health and welfare of service users, and as to the facilities and services that are to be provided. Provision is also made about record keeping, the staffing of homes, the fitness of workers, and about complaints.

Part IV makes provision about the suitability of premises and fire precautions to be taken. Part V deals with the management of care homes. Regulation 24 requires the registered person to establish a system for reviewing and improving the quality of care provided by the home. Regulation 25 imposes requirements relating to the home's financial position. Regulation 26 requires the registered provider to visit the home as prescribed. Part VI makes special provision which applies where children are accommodated at the home.

Part VII deals with miscellaneous matters including the giving of notices to the Commission. Regulation 43 provides for offences. A breach of the regulations specified in regulation 43 may found an offence on the part of the registered person. However, no prosecution may be brought unless the Commission has first given the registered person a notice which sets out in what respect it is alleged he is not complying with a regulation, and what action the Commission considers it is necessary for him to take in order to comply. The notice must specify a time period for compliance, not exceeding three months.

Notes:

[1] 2000 c. 14. The powers are exercisable by the appropriate Minister, who is defined in section 121(1), in relation to England, Scotland and Northern Ireland, as the Secretary of State. *See* section 121(1) for the definitions of "prescribed" and "regulations".back

[2] *See* section 22(9) of the Care Standards Act 2000 for the requirement to consult.back

[3] 10 & 11 Geo.6 c. 41.back

[4] 1977 c. 49.back

[5] 1997 c. 46.back

[6] 1999 c. 8.back

[7] 1977 c. 49.back

[8] *See* section 5 of the National Health Service and Community Care Act 1990 (c. 19) as amended by paragraph 69 of Schedule 1 to the Health Authorities Act 1995 (c. 17) and section 13(1) of the Health Act 1999 (c. 8).back

[9] 1992 c. 13.back

[10] S.I. 2001/3967.back

[11] 1997 c. 50. Section 115(5)(ea) was inserted by the Care Standards Act 2000, section 104, on a date to be appointed. Sections 113 and 115, as amended, have not yet been brought into force.back

[12] A position is within section 115(3) if it involves regularly caring for, training, supervising or being in sole charge of persons aged under 18. A position is within section 115(4) if it is of a kind specified in regulations and involves regularly caring for, training, supervising or being in sole charge of persons aged 18 or over.back

[13] Section 113(3A) and 115(6A) are added to the Police Act 1997 by section 8 of the Protection of Children Act 1999 (c. 14), and amended by sections 104 and 116 of, and paragraph 25 of Schedule 4 to, the Care Standards Act 2000. Sections 113(3C) and 115(6B) are added to the Police Act 1997 by section 90 of the Care Standards Act 2000 on a date to be appointed.back

[14] 1974 c. 53.back

[15] S.I. 1975/1023. Relevant amending instruments are S.I. 1986/1249, 1986/2268, 2001/1192.back

ISBN 0 11 039231 0

National Minimum Standards for Care Homes for Adults (18–65)

Introduction

Aims

This document sets out National Minimum Standards for Care Homes for Adults (18–65), which form the basis on which the new National Care Standards Commission (NCSC) will determine whether such care homes meet the needs, and secure the welfare and social inclusion, of the people who live there.

The national minimum standards set out in this document are core standards which apply to all care homes providing accommodation and nursing or personal care for adults aged 18–65 and Supplementary Standards for young people aged 16 and 17 who have:

- physical disabilities
- sensory disabilities
- learning disabilities
- autistic spectrum disorders
- mental health problems
- alcohol or substance misuse problems
- HIV/AIDS
- dual and/or complex multiple disabilities, including those who are deafblind.

The standards will apply to homes for which registration as care homes is required, including currently registered residential care and nursing homes, small homes, new facilities, local authority homes and establishments currently exempted under the Registered Homes Act 1984 (for example Charter Homes).

While broad in scope, these standards acknowledge the unique and complex needs of individuals and the additional specific knowledge, skills and facilities needed in order for a care home to deliver an individually tailored and comprehensive service. Certain of the standards do not apply to pre-existing homes including local authority homes, 'Royal Charter' homes and other homes not previously required to register.

The standards do not apply to independent hospitals, hospices, clinics or establishments registered to take patients detained under the Mental Health Act 1983. Standards for these services have been published separately.

These standards, and the regulatory framework within which they operate, should be viewed in the context of the Government's overall policy objectives for independence, choice and inclusion. A variety of specialist provision will be required to help achieve these objectives. Good quality care homes have an important part to play in that provision.

Small Homes

The standards and regulations do not distinguish between small homes for fewer than four persons and larger homes. Consultation during the development of the standards indicated that there was, in practice, very little difference between homes for three persons and those accommodating four, five or six service users. The intention in each type of setting was to achieve a domestic-scale environment and the standards have been drafted to reflect this intention.

Adult Placements

There are separate National Minimum Standards and Regulations. The National Minimum Standards for Adult Placements are now not included here. The Department of Health will be publishing these separately.

Supplementary Standards for Care Homes Accommodating Young People Aged 16 and 17

Currently, care homes for children with disabilities are registered under the Registered Homes Act 1984. This will change under the Care Standards Act, and such homes will be registered as children's homes if they fall within the definition of a children's home in the Act.

However, we know from current provision that some services straddle both care groups. We wish to establish a framework that applies to those services catering for young people in transition. For example, young people with learning disabilities aged 16–25, for whom specific services to promote independence have been set up. A similar group might be young people with physical and/or complex disabilities.

These Standards therefore include supplementary standards for care homes accommodating young people aged 16–17. These should be read in conjunction with the main standards.

Care homes should not accommodate children under the age of 16.

Regulatory Context

These standards are published by the Secretary of State for Health in accordance with section 23 of the Care Standards Act 2000 (CSA). They will apply from 1 June 2003, unless otherwise stated in any standard.

The Care Standards Act created the National Care Standards Commission (NCSC), an independent non-governmental public body, which regulates social and health care services previously regulated by local councils and health authorities. In addition, it extended the scope of regulation significantly to other services not previously registered, including domiciliary care agencies, fostering agencies and residential family centres.

The CSA sets out a broad range of regulation making powers covering, amongst other matters, the management, staff, premises and conduct of social and independent healthcare establishments and agencies.

Under the Care Standards Act, the Secretary of State for Health has powers to publish statements of National Minimum Standards. In assessing whether a care home conforms to the Care Homes Regulations 2001, which are mandatory, the National Care Standards Commission must take the standards into account. However, the Commission may also take into account any other factors it considers reasonable or relevant to do so.

Compliance with national minimum standards is not itself enforceable, but compliance with regulations is enforceable subject to national standards being taken into account.

The Commission may conclude that a care home has been in breach of the regulations even though the home largely meets the standards. The Commission also has discretion to conclude that the regulations have been complied with by means other than those set out in the national minimum standards.

Structure and Approach

The National Minimum Standards for Care Homes for Adults (18–65) focus on achievable outcomes for service users – that is, the impact on the individual of the facilities and services of the home. The standards are grouped under the following key topics which highlight aspects of individuals' lives identified during the stakeholder consultation as most important to service users:

- **Choice of home**
- **Individual needs and choices**
- **Lifestyle**
- **Personal and healthcare support**
- **Concerns, complaints and protection**
- **Environment**

- **Staffing**

- **Conduct and management of the home**

Each topic is prefaced by a statement which sets out the rationale for the standards that follow. Each standard is preceded by a statement of the intended outcome for service users to be achieved by the care home. The standards themselves are numbered and the full set of numbered paragraphs needs to be met in order to achieve compliance with the standard.

While the standards are qualitative – they provide a tool for judging the quality of life of service users – they are also measurable. Regulators will look for evidence that standards are being met and a good quality of life enjoyed by service users through:

- discussions with service users, families and friends, staff and managers, and others;

- observation of daily life in the home; and

- scrutiny of written policies, procedures, and records.

The involvement of lay assessors in inspections – including people with disabilities, mental health problems or who misuse substances – will help ensure a focus on outcomes for, and quality of life of, service users.

The following cross-cutting themes underpin the drafting of the National Minimum Standards for Care Homes for Adults (18 -65):

- **Focus on service users.** Modernising Social Services (1998) called for standards that 'focus on the key areas that most affect the quality of life experienced by service users, as well as physical standards' [4.48]. The consultation process for developing the standards, and recent research, confirm the importance of this emphasis on results for service users. In applying the standards, regulators will look for evidence that the facilities, resources, policies, activities and services of the home lead to positive outcomes for and the active participation of service users; and for people with learning disabilities, are consistent with the principles of rights, independence, choice and inclusion set out in *Valuing People*.

- **Fitness for purpose.** The regulatory powers provided by the CSA are designed to ensure that care home managers, staff and premises are 'fit for their purpose'. In applying the standards, regulators will look for evidence that a home – whether providing a long-term placement, short-term rehabilitation, nursing care or specialist service – is successful in achieving its stated aims and objectives.

- **Comprehensiveness.** Life in a care home is made up of a range of services and facilities which may be of greater or lesser importance to different service users. In applying the standards, regulators will consider how the total service package offered by the care home contributes to the overall personal and health care needs and preferences of service users, and how the home works with other services/professionals to ensure the individual's inclusion in the community.

- **Positive choice.** The consultation process confirms that some people live in care homes not through informed, positive choice but as a last resort. In applying the standards, regulators will look for evidence that service users are admitted to a home, and remain in a home, because that is where they want to be and where their needs can best be met.

- **Meeting assessed needs.** The assessment and service user plan carried out in the care home should be based on the care management individual plan and determination of registered nursing input (where relevant) produced by local social services and NHS staff where they are purchasing the service. The needs of privately funded service users should be assessed by the care home prior to a place being offered. In applying the standards, inspectors will look for evidence that care homes meet assessed needs of service users and that individuals' changing needs continue to be met.

- **Quality services.** The Government's modernising agenda, including the new regulatory framework, aims to ensure greater assurance of quality services rather than having to live with second best. In applying the standards, regulators will seek evidence of a commitment to continuous improvement, quality services, support, accommodation and facilities which assure a good quality of life and health for service users.

- **Quality workforce.** Competent, well-trained managers and staff are fundamental to achieving good quality care for service users. The Sector Skills Council for social care, TOPSS, is developing national occupational standards for care staff, including induction competencies and foundation programmes. In applying the standards, regulators will look for evidence that registered managers and staff achieve TOPSS requirements and comply with any code of practice published by the General Social Care Council.

Context and Purpose

These standards, and the regulatory framework within which they operate, should be viewed in the context of the Government's overall policy objectives for adult residential care. The standards have been prepared in response to extensive consultation and aim to be realistic, proportionate, fair and transparent. They provide minimum standards, below which no provider is expected to operate, and are designed to ensure the protection of service users and safeguard and promote their health, welfare and quality of life.

1

Choice of Home

INTRODUCTION TO STANDARDS 1 TO 5

The standards in Section 1 cover the process by which an individual chooses a care home that will meet his/her needs.

During the consultation meetings, existing and prospective service users from all user groups stressed the importance of having sufficient information about, and opportunities to consider, different options for meeting their accommodation and support requirements. Many felt they had been slotted into existing vacancies or that assumptions had been made about the service that would suit them. Prospective service users will want to make positive choices about the quite different styles and approaches of accommodation and support, considering for example size and location; staff and current residents; religious affiliation; treatment philosophies; specialist services and activity programmes.

Care homes are expected to produce information – the Statement of Purpose and Service Users' Guide – about their services and facilities in a way that is accessible to those for whom the service is intended. Where feasible, trial visits will also help prospective service users judge whether a particular home will be suitable. As well as having clear information about possible care homes, prospective service users should feel confident that their needs and aspirations are fully understood by the home's staff and manager and that the home they choose will be able and accountable to deliver the services it undertakes to provide.

Stakeholder consultation highlighted the importance of individual needs assessment in the process of choosing the right home. While not seeking to hold proprietors/managers to account for the actions of others, the National Minimum Standards require that they can demonstrate that a full, professional assessment – either the single Care Management assessment or the home's own assessment – has been carried out for each individual entering the home, except in the case of emergency. Managers should be able to provide evidence that service users have been genuinely involved in the assessment process, with appropriate support and/or advocacy.

Managers should also show that no admission is made unless the home has the quality and quantity of staff and the resources adequately to meet the person's assessed needs as determined by assessment. The proprietor is expected to be accountable for delivery of promised services under a written contract between the care home and the service user which sets out the terms and conditions of residency and service provision (including a Service User Plan, see section 2), and the rights and responsibilities of both parties.

See also:

Mental Health Foundation (1996), *Building Expectations.*

Office of Fair Trading (1998), *Choosing a Care Home.*

DH (2001), Single Assessment *Process Consultation Document.*

Information

OUTCOME

Prospective service users have the information they need to make an informed choice about where to live.

STANDARD 1

1.1 **The registered person produces an up-to-date statement of purpose setting out the aims, objectives and philosophy of the home, its services and facilities, and terms and conditions; and provides each service user with a service users' guide to the home. The statement of purpose should clearly set out the physical environment standards met by the home in relation to standards 24.2, 24.9, 25.3, 25.5, 27.2, 27.4 and 28.2; and a summary of this information should appear in the service users' guide.**

1.2 The services users' guide sets out clear and accessible information for service users including:

i   A summary of the purpose of the home;

ii   A description of the support and facilities (including any specialist services and strategies for communicating with service users);

iii A description of the individual accommodation and communal space provided;

iv   The number of places provided and the people for whom the service is intended;

v   Relevant qualifications and experience of the registered provider, manager and staff;

vi   Key contract terms covering admission, occupancy and termination of contract;

vii Fees charged, what they cover, And the cost of 'extras';

viii Service users' views of the home (users surveys); and

ix   A copy of the complaints procedure, and information about how to contact the local office of the NCSC and local social services and healthcare authorities.

1.3   A copy of the most recent inspection report is made available to service users and their families.

1.4   The service users' guide, inspection report and other information about the home are available in formats suitable for the people for whom the home is intended (e.g. appropriate languages, pictures, video, audio or explanation).

Needs Assessment

OUTCOME

Prospective service users' individual aspirations and needs are assessed.

STANDARD 2

2.1   New service users are admitted only on the basis of a full assessment undertaken by people competent to do so, involving the prospective service user, using an appropriate communication method and with an independent advocate as appropriate.

2.2   For individuals referred through Care Management, the registered manager obtains a summary of the single Care Management (health and social services) assessment – integrated with the Care Programme Approach (CPA) for people with mental health problems – and a copy of the single Care Plan.

2.3   For individuals who are self-funding and without a Care Management Assessment/Care Plan, the home carries out a needs assessment (meeting the person in his/her own living environment where possible) covering:

i.   suitable accommodation and personal support;

ii.   meaningful education, training and/or occupation;

iii.   family/social contact;

iv.   assessment and management of risk;

v.   adequate income;

vi.   cultural and faith needs;

vii.   physical and mental health care;

viii.   specific condition-related needs and specialist input;

ix.   provision of disability equipment, including arrangements for payment and supply;

x.   treatment/rehabilitation programme;

xi.   method of communication; and

xii.   compatibility with others living in the home.

2.4 The home develops with each prospective service user an individual Service User Plan based on the Care Management Assessment and Care Plan or the home's own needs assessment (see Standard 6 'Service User Plan').

2.5 Any potential restrictions on choice, freedom, services or facilities – based on specialist needs and risk and/or required by a treatment programme – likely to become part of a prospective service user's individual Plan, are discussed and agreed with the prospective service user during assessment.

2.6 The registered nursing input required by service users in homes providing nursing care is determined by NHS registered nurses using a recognised assessment tool, according to Department of Health guidance.

2.7 Rehabilitation and therapeutic needs are assessed by state registered health professionals using regulated assessment methods.

2.8 Family carers' interests and needs are taken into account, subject to the service user's agreement.

Meeting Needs

OUTCOME

Prospective service users know that the home they choose will meet their needs and aspirations.

STANDARD 3

3.1 The registered person can demonstrate the home's capacity to meet the assessed needs (including specialist needs) of individuals admitted to the home.

3.2 All specialised services offered (e.g. services for people with mental health problems, sensory impairment, physical disabilities, learning disabilities, substance misuse problems, transition services, intermediate or respite care) are demonstrably based on current good practice, and reflect relevant specialist and clinical guidance.

3.3 The needs and preferences of specific minority ethnic communities, and social/cultural or religious groups catered for, are recognised and met.

3.4 Staff individually and collectively have the skills and experience to deliver the services and care which the home offers to provide.

3.5 The home demonstrates that staff can communicate effectively with prospective service users using the individual's preferred mode of communication.

3.6 Prospective service users entering a home for a period of specialist treatment, rehabilitation or education are provided with clear information about the purpose, duration and requirements of the programme.

3.7 The home confirms that prospective service users are informed about independent advocacy/self-advocacy schemes throughout the process of choosing a home.

3.8 The home does not offer a place to someone whose needs it cannot meet, or with whom it cannot develop effective communication, and provides a written or other suitable explanation for refusal to the prospective service user (and Care Manager where applicable).

3.9 The home does not admit into long-term care any service user placed for intermediate/short-term care, unless and until the requirements regarding information, assessment and individual planning (Standards 1, 2, 3 and 6) are met. See also Standards 24.5 and 29.4 (facilities); and 33.5 (staffing).

3.10 In homes providing planned respite, the statement of purpose, assessment process and individual Service User Plan are designed to meet the specific needs of the people for whom the service is intended.

Introductory Visits

OUTCOME

Prospective service users have an opportunity to visit and to 'test drive' the home.

STANDARD 4

4.1 The registered manager invites prospective service users to visit the home on an introductory basis before making a decision to move there, and unplanned admissions are avoided where possible.

4.2 A minimum half-day (preferably including overnight) visit to the home is offered, including an opportunity for the prospective service user (with family, friends, advocate, interpreters as appropriate) to:

    i. meet service users (without staff or carers present if appropriate);

    ii. meet staff (without carers present if appropriate);

    iii. view the room in which the person would live and the common areas and grounds;

    iv. have a meal;

    v. discuss how the home can meet the person's requirements; and

    vi. see the kind of records kept about service users.

4.3 A minimum three month 'settling in' period of residence is offered for long-term placements, followed by a review with the service user of the trial placement, during which existing users are consulted about the compatibility of the prospective new resident.

4.4 Emergency admission does not imply the right or requirement to stay in the same home, and service users placed in an emergency are fully assessed and relocated if the care provided is not appropriate to their needs.

4.5 When an emergency admission is made, the home undertakes to inform the service user within 48 hours about key aspects, rules and routines of the service, and to meet all other admission criteria set out in Standards 2–3 within five working days.

Contract

OUTCOME

Each service user has an individual written contract or statement of terms and conditions with the home.

STANDARD 5

5.1 **The registered manager develops and agrees with each prospective service user a written and costed contract/statement of terms and conditions between the home and the service user.**

5.2 The contract specifies:

i. rooms to be occupied;

ii. terms and conditions of occupancy including period of notice (e.g. long-term home, short-term placement, planned respite, intermediate care/rehabilitation);

iii. personal support, facilities and services provided, including any specialist services/therapeutic intervention, and any policies or rules which may limit personal freedom;

iv fees charged, what they cover, and when they must be paid and by whom, and the cost of facilities or services not covered by fees;

v. rights and responsibilities of both parties, and who is liable if there is a breach of contract;

vi. a copy of the Service User Plan (see Standard 6) outlining the action/activities to achieve personal goals and lifestyle aspirations;

vii. arrangements for reviewing needs and progress, and updating the Service User Plan; and

viii elements of the Care Management Care Plan (where applicable) which are to be provided outside of the home.

5.3 Service users are supported by family, friends and/or advocate, as appropriate, when drawing up the contract.

5.4 The contract is in a format/language appropriate to each service user's needs, and/or reasonable efforts have been made to explain the contract to the service user.

5.5 The service user has a copy of the contract, which has been signed by the service user and the registered manager.

Individual Needs and Choices

INTRODUCTION TO STANDARDS 6 TO 10

The standards in Section 2 cover issues of decision making, participation, risk taking and confidentiality that need to be addressed by care homes in order for service users to achieve independent lifestyles.

Younger adults who took part in the consultation events expressed their frustration at being denied opportunities to make major life decisions as well as everyday choices. They stressed the importance of information and support, including access to independent advocacy, to help them express their views and lead their lives as they choose.

These standards start from the premise that service users should be enabled to take control of their own lives. Supporting those with intellectual impairment and/or limited communication skills to make decisions, is the responsibility of home managers and staff. In homes for people who misuse drugs or alcohol, restrictions on decision making may be necessary in the initial stages of a treatment programme.

Proprietors will be expected to set out clearly in the home's Statement of Purpose the people for whom the service is intended, demonstrating how they will enable service users to make informed decisions, and they will be accountable for fulfilling their claims. This includes support to understand available options and the right to take risks and to make – and learn from – poor choices. While care homes cannot ensure sufficient provision for independent advocacy, they should undertake to help service users access local advocacy and support schemes. The standards permit limitations on individual choice and freedom only following assessment, in discussion with the service user, and as recorded (and reviewed) in the Service User Plan.

Key to achieving an individually appropriate lifestyle is the Service User Plan, determined by assessment and drawn up between the home and the service user. It puts the individual at the centre of service delivery by the care home. The Plan should reflect the needs, aspirations and goals of the individual, set out the services to be provided by the care home to meet needs and achieve goals, and develop as the service user's life and circumstances change. Services are expected to be delivered by the home in accordance with the individual Service User Plan, which becomes the yardstick for judging whether appropriate support is being delivered.

Staff may be in receipt of considerable personal information about the people they support: these standards require that care homes ensure that information given in confidence by and about service users is handled appropriately.

See also:

DH (2002), *Guidance on the Use of Physical Interventions.*

Data Protection Act 1998

S Dowson (1990), *Keeping it safe.*

A Wertheimer (1998), *Citizen Advocacy.*

P Fitton (1994), *Listen to Me.*

J Morris (2000), *Hurtling into the Void.*

Values into Action (2001), *Who's in control? Decision-making by people with learning difficulties who have high support needs.* London: VIA

Service User Plan

OUTCOME

Service users know their assessed and changing needs and personal goals are reflected in their individual Plan.

STANDARD 6

6.1   **The registered manager develops and agrees with each service user an individual Plan, which may include treatment and rehabilitation, describing the services and facilities to be provided by the home, and how these services will meet current and changing needs and aspirations and achieve goals.**

6.2   The Plan is generated from the single Care Management Assessment/Care Plan or the home's own assessment, and covers all aspects of personal and social support and healthcare needs as set out in Standard 2.

6.3   The Plan sets out how current and anticipated specialist requirements will be met (for example through positive planned interventions; rehabilitation and therapeutic programmes; structured environments; development of language and communication; adaptations and equipment; one-to-one communication support).

6.4   The Plan describes any restrictions on choice and freedom (agreed with the service user) imposed by a specialist programme (e.g. a treatment programme for drug or alcohol misusers); for mental health service users, in accordance with the Care Programme Approach and in some instances the Mental Health Act 1983).

6.5   The Plan establishes individualised procedures for service users likely to be aggressive or cause harm or self-harm, focusing on positive behaviour, ability and willingness.

6.6 The Plan is drawn up with the involvement of the service user together with family, friends and/or advocate as appropriate, and relevant agencies/specialists.

6.7 The Plan is made available in a language and format the service user can understand (e.g. visual, graphic, simple printed English, deafblind manual, explanation, British Sign Language video), and is held by the service user unless there are clear (and recorded) reasons not to do so.

6.8 A key worker (or personal tutor in specialist colleges; designated nurse if receiving nursing care) who can communicate with the individual and appreciates his/her racial and/or cultural heritage is allocated for each service user, with the full involvement of the service user.

6.9 The service user is made aware of the respective roles and responsibilities of the Care Manager/CPA Care Co-ordinator, key worker and/or advocate, and knows how to contact them.

6.10 The Plan is reviewed with the service user (involving significant professionals, and family, friends and advocates as agreed with the service user) at the request of the service user or at least every six months and updated to reflect changing needs; and agreed changes are recorded and actioned.

Decision Making

OUTCOME

Service users make decisions about their lives with assistance as needed.

STANDARD 7

7.1 Staff respect service users' right to make decisions, and that right is limited only through the assessment process, involving the service user, and as recorded in the individual Service User Plan.

7.2 Staff provide service users with the information, assistance and communication support they need to make decisions about their own lives.

7.3 Staff help service users, if they wish, to find and participate in local independent advocacy/self-advocacy groups and/or to find peer support from someone who shares the person's disability, heritage or aspirations.

7.4 Staff can demonstrate how individual choices have been made; and record instances when decisions are made by others, and why.

7.5 Service users manage their own finances; where support and tuition are needed, the reasons for, and manner, of support are documented and reviewed.

7.6 Limitations on facilities, choice or human rights to prevent self-harm or self-neglect, or abuse or harm to others, are made only in the person's best interest, consistent with the purpose of the service and the home's duties and responsibilities under law.

7.7 Where a Department of Work and Pensions appointee or other agent is necessary, the appointee/agent is independent from the service. If no independent agent is available, the registered manager may be appointed agent, and in this case:

    i.   the registration authority is notified on inspection; and

    ii.   records are kept of all incoming and outgoing payments, and independently audited/monitored.

Participation

OUTCOME

Service users are consulted on, and participate in, all aspects of life in the home.

STANDARD 8

8.1 The registered manager ensures that service users are offered opportunities to participate in the day to day running of the home and to contribute to the development and review of policies, procedures and services.

8.2 The home provides service users with comprehensive, accessible, understandable and up to date information, in suitable formats, about its policies, procedures, activities and services; and appropriate communication support.

8.3 Service users have opportunities to participate (and are enabled to participate through e.g. provision of interpreters and translators, independent advocates, training, documents in appropriate formats) in activities which enable them to influence key decisions in the home, for example:

    i.   joining staff meetings, policy groups and other forums;

    ii.   representation in management structures;

    iii.   involvement in selection of staff and of other service users; and

    iv.   user satisfaction questionnaires, individual and group discussion (see Standard 39– 'Quality Assurance').

8.4 Changes are made to the home's statement of purpose only in consultation with existing service users.

8.5 Service users receive feedback about the outcomes of their involvement and participation.

Risk Taking

OUTCOME

Service users are supported to take risks as part of an independent lifestyle.

STANDARD 9

9.1 **Staff enable service users to take responsible risks, ensuring they have good information on which to base decisions, within the context of the service user's individual Plan and of the home's risk assessment and risk management strategies.**

9.2 Risk is assessed prior to admission according to health and social services protocols and in discussion with the service user and relevant specialists; and risk management strategies are agreed, recorded in the individual Plan, and reviewed.

9.3 Action is taken to minimize identified risks and hazards, and service users are given training about their personal safety, to avoid limiting the service user's preferred activity or choice.

9.4 The home responds promptly to unexplained absences by service users according to written procedure.

Confidentiality

OUTCOME

Service users know that information about them is handled appropriately, and that their confidences are kept.

STANDARD 10

10.1 **Staff respect information given by service users in confidence, and handle information about services users, in accordance with the home's written policies and procedures and the Data Protection Act 1998, and in the best interests of the service user.**

10.2 Service users and their families have access to the home's policy and procedures on confidentiality and on dealing with breaches of confidentiality, and staff explain and/or ensure service users understand the policy.

10.3 Service users' individual records are accurate, secure and confidential.

10.4 Staff know when information given them in confidence must be shared with their manager or others.

10.5 Information given in confidence is not shared with families/friends against the service user's wishes.

10.6 The home gives a statement on confidentiality to partner agencies, setting out the principles governing the sharing of information.

3
Lifestyle

INTRODUCTION TO STANDARDS 11 TO 17

The standards in section 3 cover the elements of service and support in care homes that enable service users to maintain appropriate and fulfilling lifestyles in and outside the home.

For younger adults, a place to live and personal support are the starting point for achieving independence. Service users attending the consultation meetings shared their aspirations to live ordinary and meaningful lives appropriate to their peer group, and to participate in and contribute to the communities where they live. Lifestyle aspirations will naturally vary according to the person's age, culture, experience and interest as well as his/her disability or illness. Opportunities for personal development and independence training; for appropriate education and training, paid work or meaningful occupation; and for integration into community life and leisure activities, were all high priorities for people taking part in the consultation meetings. Care home staff will have a key role to play in supporting service users to live fulfilling lives outside as well as within the home. For people with substance misuse problems, curtailment of lifestyle preferences may be required at the start of the rehabilitation process.

Younger adults need to be able to judge how a home will enable them to achieve their goals. The home's Statement of Purpose and Service Users' Guide will give prospective residents an overall picture of the home's philosophy and style of living, the structure and organisation of daily routines and activities, and specialist provision. The individual Service User Plan will detail how the person's assessed needs, preferences and goals will be met by the home.

Participants also highlighted the importance of developing and maintaining personal and family relationships while resident in a care home, and managers will be expected to have policies and knowledge, appropriate to the people living in the home, about supporting relationships and protecting against abuse.

Care homes will also be judged by the way their house rules and daily routines – e.g. forms of address, entry to rooms, opening mail, performance of housekeeping tasks, provision of meals – respect service users' individuality, dignity and privacy and promote their wellbeing and independence. Care homes should be clear about the extent to which service users' involvement in meal planning and preparation is possible or required, and whether individual's personal, cultural/religious and medical food preferences and requirements can be observed.

See also:

DH (2001), *Valuing People.*

J Morris (2001), *'That Kind of Life'.*

MS Society and Leonard Cheshire Foundation (1988), *People with MS in Long Term Care.*

DH (2000), *Community Care (Direct Payments) Act 1996.*

B McIntosh and A Whittaker (eds) (1998), *Days of Change.*

A Wertheimer (ed) (1996), *Changing Days.*

RNID (1999), *Best Practice Standards: Social Services for Deaf and Hard of Hearing People.* London RNID.

RNIB: *National Visual Impairment Standards. Progress in sight.* Issued by the ADSS:October 2002.

Personal Development

OUTCOME

Service users have opportunities for personal development.

STANDARD 11

11.1 Staff enable service users to have opportunities to maintain and develop social, emotional, communication and independent living skills.

11.2 Service users have opportunities to learn and use practical life skills (e.g. assertion and confidence training), including user-led training.

11.3 Service users in treatment and recovery programmes receive effective, professionally validated interventions, counselling and therapy. Service users with complex multiple disabilities are offered specialist interventions and opportunities by trained staff.

11.4 Service users have opportunities to fulfil their spiritual needs.

Education and Occupation

OUTCOME

Service users are able to take part in age, peer and culturally appropriate activities.

STANDARD 12

12.1   Staff help service users to find and keep appropriate jobs, continue their education or training, and/or take part in valued and fulfilling activities.

12.2   Service users can continue to take part in activities engaged in prior to entering the home, if they wish, or re-establish activities if they change localities.

12.3   Staff help service users find out about and take up opportunities for further education, distance learning, and vocational, literacy and numeracy training.

12.4   Staff help service users to develop employment skills, and to develop and maintain links with careers advice services, local employers and job centres.

12.5   Staff help service users find out about and take up opportunities for paid, supported or volunteer jobs/therapeutic work placements or work-related training schemes.

12.6   Staff help service users with benefits/finance problems or refer appropriately. Community Links and Social Inclusion

Community Links and Social Inclusion

OUTCOME

Service users are part of the local community.

STANDARD 13

13.1   Staff support service users to become part of, and participate in, the local community in accordance with assessed needs and the individual Plans.

13.2   Staff enable service users' integration into community life through:

   i.   knowledge about, and support for, service users to make use of services, facilities and activities in the local community (e.g. shops, library, cinema, pubs, leisure centres, places of worship, cultural centres);

   ii.   awareness of service users' rights of access to public facilities under the Disability Discrimination Act 1995;

   iii.   maintaining a neighbourly relationship with the community;

   iv.   ensuring information and advice are available about local activities, support and resources offered by specialist organisations; and

v   ensuring access to transport – local public transport, accessible taxis, dial-a-ride, the home's own (unlabelled, or discreetly labelled on condition of a gift) vehicles – and support to use it, to enable service users to pursue their chosen lifestyle and activities.

13.3   Service users are enabled to be politically active and to vote.

13.4   Staff time with, and support for, service users outside the home – flexibly provided, including evenings and weekends – is a recognised part of staff duties (see Standards 31 – 'Staff roles' and 33 – 'Staff team').

13.5   The home values and seeks to reflect the racial and cultural diversity of service users and of the community in which it is located.

Leisure

OUTCOME

Service users engage in appropriate leisure activities.

STANDARD 14

14.1   Staff ensure that service users have access to, and choose from a range of, appropriate leisure activities.

14.2   Service users are encouraged and supported to pursue their own interests and hobbies.

14.3   Service users have a choice of entertainment brought in to the home.

14.4   Service users in long-term placements have as part of the basic contract price the option of a minimum seven-day annual holiday outside the home, which they help choose and plan.

14.5   Group trips are planned and chosen by users who share the same interests.

14.6   Activities arranged by the home are run by trained staff with appropriate professional support and advice.

Relationships

OUTCOME

Service users have appropriate personal, family and sexual relationships.

STANDARD 15

15.1 **Staff support service users to maintain family links and friendships inside and outside the home, subject to restrictions agreed in the individual Plan and Contract (subject to standards 2 and 6 if necessary).**

15.2 Family and friends are welcomed, and their involvement in daily routines and activities is encouraged, with the service user's agreement.

15.3 Service users choose whom they see and when; and can see visitors in their rooms and in private.

15.4 Service users have opportunities to meet people and make friends who do not have their disability/illness/addiction.

15.5 Service users can develop and maintain intimate personal relationships with people of their choice, and information and specialist guidance are provided to help the service user to make appropriate decisions.

Daily Routines

OUTCOME

Service users' rights are respected and responsibilities recognised in their daily lives.

STANDARD 16

16.1 **The daily routines and house rules promote independence, individual choice and freedom of movement, subject to restrictions agreed in the individual Plan and Contract (subject to standards 2 and 6 if necessary).**

16.2 Staff enter service users' bedrooms and bathrooms only with the individual's permission and normally in their presence, and techniques are in place (e.g. doorbells, flashing lights, according to disability) to ensure privacy for all service users.

16.3 Service users are offered a key (or suitable locking device) to their own bedroom/bathroom, which can be locked from inside and outside, and a key to the front door of the home.

16.4 Staff do not open service users' mail without their agreement.

16.5 Staff use service users' preferred form of address, which is recorded in the individual Plan.

16.6 Staff talk to and interact with service users, not exclusively with each other.

16.7 Service users choose when to be alone or in company, and when not to join an activity.

16.8 Service users have unrestricted access to the home and grounds; service users' visitors have access subject to individual and collective service user consent.

16.9 Service users' responsibility for housekeeping tasks (e.g. cooking, cleaning rooms and common areas, laundry, maintaining gardens) is specified in the Service Users' Guide and individual Plan.

16.10 Service users can keep an assistance dog (guide dogs, dogs for disabled people, and hearing dogs for deaf people); and can keep a suitable pet in agreement with the home and if it does not infringe on the safety, health or peace of others living in the home.

16.11 Rules on smoking, alcohol and drugs are clearly stated in the contract.

Meals and Mealtimes

OUTCOME
Service users are offered a healthy diet and enjoy their meals and mealtimes.

STANDARD 17

17.1 The registered person promotes service users' health and wellbeing by ensuring the supply of nutritious, varied, balanced and attractively presented meals in a congenial setting and at flexible times.

17.2 Service users are offered a choice of suitable menus, which meet their dietary and cultural needs, and which respect their individual preferences.

17.3 Meals are offered three times daily including at least one cooked meal; and a range of drinks and snacks to meet individual needs are available at all times.

17.4 Service users are actively supported to help plan, prepare and serve meals.

17.5 Service users can choose where and when to eat, and whether to eat alone or with others including staff.

17.6 The preparation and serving of food respects service users' cultural and religious requirements.

17.7 Mealtimes are relaxed, unrushed, and flexible to suit service users' activities and schedules.

17.8 Service users' nutritional needs are assessed and regularly reviewed including risk factors associated with low weight, obesity, and eating and drinking disorders.

17.9 Service users who need help to eat or are fed artificially are assisted appropriately while maintaining choice of when, where and what they eat; and assisted to choose appropriate eating aids.

4

Personal and Healthcare Support

INTRODUCTION TO STANDARDS 18 TO 21

Section 4 sets out standards for ensuring that care homes provide appropriate personal and healthcare support to service users, and deal sensitively with issues of ageing, illness and death.

The way in which support is given is a key issue for younger adults in care homes. During the consultation programme service users stressed the need for personal support that is flexible, consistent, reliable and responsive to their changing needs. For some (e.g. those with severe physical disabilities) moving and transferring by staff is critical to their independence and autonomy; for others (e.g. people with mental health problems) emotional and psychological support may be paramount. These standards require staff to respect service users' preferences, and expert knowledge, about their individual personal needs when providing support including intimate personal care.

Service users have the right to good quality physical and mental health care wherever they are living. Care homes will be expected to support younger adults to manage their own healthcare (including visual, hearing, oral and continence care) and to access NHS community facilities, while ensuring that vulnerable individuals' health is reviewed and maintained. Specialist health, nursing and dietary requirements set out in the Service User's Plan should be observed. Staff will also support service users to manage their own medication within the framework of the home's risk management policy and in compliance with professional guidance and the law.

Different homes will have different competencies and specialisms and these should be clearly set out in their Statement of Purpose. The individual Service User Plan will detail key aspects of how an individual should be supported. Managers/proprietors should only accept a service user whose assessed personal, healthcare and nursing care needs the home's staff are qualified to meet, and evidence of this will be required.

Most younger adults choosing a home will be concerned primarily with their lives and futures. However, service users and their families should be clear about how ageing, illness and death will be handled by the care home. Those approaching the transition to older age will need to know whether they can stay in the home when they reach age 65, and if they become ill or more disabled. They, and others with deteriorating/terminal disability or illness, will want to know that their last days will be spent in comfort and with dignity and that their wishes will be observed.

See also:

Diabetic Association (July 1999), *Guidelines of Practice.*

National Council for Hospice and Specialist Palliative Care Services (1997), *Changing Gear.*

Royal Pharmaceutical Society (2001) guidelines; United Kingdom Central Council for Nursing, Midwifery and Health Visiting (1992) guidelines; Misuse of Drugs (Safe Custody) Regulations 1973; Medicines Act 1968.

Personal Support

OUTCOME

Service users receive personal support in the way they prefer and require.

STANDARD 18

18.1 Staff provide sensitive and flexible personal support and nursing care to maximise service users' privacy, dignity, independence and control over their lives.

18.2 Service users' preferences about how they are guided, moved, supported and transferred are complied with, and reasons for not doing so are explained and recorded.

18.3 Personal support is provided in private, and intimate care by a person of the same gender where possible and if the service user wishes.

18.4 Times for getting up/going to bed, baths, meals and other activities are flexible (including evening and weekends), subject to restrictions agreed in the individual Plan (Standards 2 and 6 refer).

18.5 Where needed, guidance and support regarding personal hygiene (e.g. to wash, shave) is provided.

18.6 Service users choose their own clothes, hairstyle and makeup and their appearance reflects their personality.

18.7 Service users have some choice of staff who work with them, such as staff from the same ethnic, religious or cultural background or the same gender.

18.8 Service users have the technical aids and equipment they need for maximum independence (which staff are trained to operate as needed), determined by professional assessment, reviewed and changed or replaced promptly as the service user's needs change, and regularly serviced.

18.9 Service users receive additional, specialist support and advice as needed from physiotherapists, occupational therapists, speech therapists and others, for e.g. positioning or modification of equipment.

18.10 General and psychiatric nursing care is provided or supervised by registered nurses as specified in the individual Plan, monitored and recorded, and regularly reviewed.

18.11 Staff ensure consistency and continuity of support for service users through:

i. designated key workers (whom service users have helped choose);

ii. individual working records setting out the preferred routine, likes or dislikes of service users who cannot easily communicate their needs and preferences; and

iii partnerships with advocates, family, friends and relevant professionals outside the home, subject to the service user's consent.

Healthcare

OUTCOME

Service users' physical and emotional health needs are met.

STANDARD 19

19.1 The registered person ensures that the healthcare needs of service users are assessed and recognised and that procedures are in place to address them.

19.2 Service users are supported and facilitated to take control of and manage their own healthcare, including:

i. support to gain access to up to date information and advice about general health issues e.g. continence, contraception, routine screening;

ii. support to manage their own medical conditions (e.g. diabetes) where feasible;

iii. support to choose their GP, to make decisions about their own healthcare/medical treatment, and to seek a second medical opinion;

iv. support to access NHS healthcare facilities in the locality – primary care team, dentist, optician, audiologist, chiropodist/podiatrist, therapists, community nurses and specialist nurses (e.g. diabetes specialist nurse, mental health nurse), complementary therapies;

v. support to attend outpatient and other appointments; and

vi. support to access independent interpreters.

19.3 Service users' health is monitored and potential complications and problems are identified and dealt with at an early stage, including prompt referral to an appropriate specialist.

19.4 Service users are offered minimum annual health checks (including attention to vision and hearing; medication; illness/disability unrelated to primary disability/condition).

19.5   Visits to service users from medical/health care practitioners take place in private.

Medication

OUTCOME

Service users, retain, administer and control their own medication where appropriate, and are protected by the home's policies and procedures for dealing with medicines.

STANDARD 20

20.1   The registered manager and staff encourage and support service users to retain, administer and control their own medication, within a risk management framework, and comply with the home's policy and procedure for the receipt, recording, storage, handling, administration and disposal of medicines.

20.2   Service users' consent to medication is obtained and recorded in the individual Plan.

20.3   The service user, following assessment as able to self-administer medication, has a lockable space in which to store medication, to which suitably trained, designated care staff may have access with the service user's permission.

20.4   Records are kept of all medicines received, administered and leaving the home or disposed of to ensure that there is no mishandling.

20.5   A record is maintained of current medication for each service user (including those self-administering).

20.6   Medicines in the custody of the home are handled according to the requirements of the Medicines Act 1968, guidelines from the Royal Pharmaceutical Society of Great Britain, the requirements of the Misuse of Drugs Act 1971 and nursing staff abide by the UKCC Standards for the administration of medicines.

20.7   Controlled drugs administered by staff are stored in a metal cupboard, which complies with current regulations and guidance issued by the Royal Pharmaceutical Society of Great Britain.

20.8   Medicines, including controlled drugs, for service users in care homes providing nursing care, are administered by a medical practitioner or registered nurse.

20.9   In residential care homes all medicines, including controlled drugs (except those for self-administration), are administered by designated and appropriately trained staff. The administration of controlled drugs is witnessed by another designated appropriately trained member of staff.

20.10   The training for care staff must be accredited and must include:

    i.   basic knowledge of how medicines are used and how to recognise and deal with problems in use; and

    ii.   the principles behind all aspects of the home's policy on medicines handling and records.

20.11 Receipt, administration and disposal of controlled drugs are recorded in a controlled drugs register.

20.12 The registered manager seeks information and advice from a pharmacist regarding medicines policies within the home and medicines dispensed for individuals in the home.

20.13 Staff monitor the condition of the service user on medication and call in the GP if staff are concerned about any change in condition that may be a result of medication, and prompt the review of medication on a regular basis.

20.14 In the event of the death of a service user, medicines should be retained for a period of seven days in case there is a coroner's inquest.

Ageing and Death

OUTCOME

The ageing, illness and death of a service user are handled with respect and as the individual would wish.

STANDARD 21

21.1 The registered manager and staff deal with the ageing, illness and death of a service user with sensitivity and respect.

21.2 Service users and their family and friends know (as agreed in the individual Plan and regularly reviewed) whether they will be able to remain in the home when they grow older and/or if they require nursing care.

21.3 The service user's wishes concerning terminal care and death are discussed and carried out, including observation of religious and cultural customs.

21.4 The service user's family and friends are involved (if that is what the service user wants) in planning for and dealing with growing older, terminal illness and death.

21.5 Palliative care, practical assistance and advice, and bereavement counselling are provided by trained professionals/specialist agencies if the service user wishes.

21.6 Service users are able to receive treatment and care and to die in their own room, if that is their wish, unless there is a medical reason for an alternative setting.

21.7 The changing needs of service users with deteriorating conditions or dementia – for personal support or technical aids – are reviewed and met swiftly to ensure the individual retains maximum control.

21.8 Other service users (and staff) living in the home are supported to deal with the illness or death of a service user.

5

Concerns, Complaints and Protection

INTRODUCTION TO STANDARDS 22 TO 23

Section 5 sets out standards for responding to concerns and complaints and for ensuring that service users are safe from abuse or neglect.

During the consultation meetings, service users highlighted the importance of being listened to and feeling confident that their views are seriously taken on board by the care home's staff and manager. It appeared that some service providers currently have no effective system for hearing and responding to issues raised by service users, including concerns about their treatment by staff. Filing a formal complaint is often the only course open to service users or their families, who may be reluctant to do so because they fear they will not be taken seriously or that they may be victimised or have their services withdrawn.

These standards require care home managers to have clear procedures that enable service users to make their views known, and that reassure them that appropriate action will be taken. Policies and procedures for dealing with suspicion or evidence of physical, financial or material, psychological or sexual abuse, neglect, self-harm or degrading behaviour should also be put in place. NCSC will look to the home's quality assurance process, including the service user survey, for evidence of an open culture and appropriate complaints procedures in the home. Complainants may make complaints directly to the NCSC.

See also:

G Bailey (1988), *Action Against Abuse.*

DH & Home Office (2000), *No Secrets.*

K Simons (1996), *I'm Not Complaining, But....*

Concerns and Complaints

OUTCOME

Service users feel their views are listened to and acted on.

STANDARD 22

22.1   The registered person ensures that there is a clear and effective complaints procedure, which includes the stages of, and time scales, for the process, and that service users know how and to whom to complain.

22.2   The registered manager and staff listen to and act on the views and concerns of service users and others, and encourage discussion and action on issues raised by service users before they develop into problems and formal complaints.

22.3   The home's complaints procedure has been given and/or explained to each service user in an appropriate language/format, including information for referring a complaint to the NCSC at any stage should the complainant wish to do so.

22.4   All complaints are responded to within 28 days.

22.5   Service users, if they wish, can make a complaint one-to-one with a staff member of their choice, and/or are helped to access local independent advocacy, independent interpreters/communication support workers and/or appropriate training.

22.6   Service users and their families are assured they will not be victimised for making a complaint.

22.7   A record is kept of all issues raised or complaints made by service users, details of any investigation, action taken and outcome; and this record is checked at least three-monthly.

Protection

OUTCOME

Service users are protected from abuse, neglect and self-harm.

STANDARD 23

23.1 **The registered person ensures that service users are safeguarded from physical, financial or material, psychological or sexual abuse, neglect, discriminatory abuse or self-harm or inhuman or degrading treatment, through deliberate intent, negligence or ignorance, in accordance with written policy.**

23.2 Robust procedures for responding to suspicion or evidence of abuse or neglect (including whistle blowing) ensure the safety and protection of service users (including passing on concerns to the NCSC), in accordance with the Public Interest Disclosure Act 1998 and Department of Health guidance No Secrets.

23.3 All allegations and incidents of abuse, and action taken, are recorded.

23.4 Staff who may be unsuitable to work with vulnerable adults are referred in accordance with the Care Standards Act for consideration for inclusion on the Protection of Children and Vulnerable Adults registers.

23.5 Physical and verbal aggression by a service user is understood and dealt with appropriately, and physical intervention is used only as a last resort by trained staff in accordance with Department of Health guidance, protects the rights and best interests of the service user, and is the minimum consistent with safety.

23.6 The home's policies and practices regarding service users' money and financial affairs ensure for example service users' access to their personal financial records, safe storage of money and valuables, consultation on finances in private, and advice on personal insurance; and preclude staff involvement in making or benefiting from service users' wills.

6

Environment

INTRODUCTION TO STANDARDS 24 TO 30

Section 6 sets out standards covering the care home's premises including individual bedrooms and shared spaces, adaptations and equipment, and hygiene.

People with disabilities and with mental health and substance abuse problems who took part in the consultation events stressed the importance of a living environment that is appropriate for their particular lifestyle and needs and accessible to relevant community facilities and services, as well as homely, clean, safe and comfortable.

While these standards do set minimum room sizes, the key requirement is that service users' own room accommodates their possessions, enables them to pursue their chosen interests and activities, and offers sufficient privacy. For someone who spends a large part of the day in his/her room or whose physical condition or occupation requires bulky equipment (e.g. a life-support unit, wheelchair, or computer), a large bedroom is of relatively greater importance than for someone who spends most daytime hours at work or college or who prefers a more communal lifestyle.

Single rooms and private bathrooms are the clear preference of service users, as are small family-scale homes. These standards require that service users are offered the option of a single room (except in homes offering rehabilitation for people who misuse alcohol or drugs, where room sharing may be an agreed part of the initial treatment process). Many homes currently recognise this as best practice and have development plans underway to provide en suite single rooms. The Department of Health intends to carry out research on the benefits to service users of multi-occupancy in homes for people who misuse drugs or alcohol. Stakeholder consultation indicated that it is preferable not to mix long-and short-term (respite) provision; managers will be required to demonstrate that doing so benefits all service users.

Respect for service users' privacy is fundamentally important, including the freedom to come and go and receive guests as they wish and to have their own door key. The privacy and autonomy of service users within the home may be limited only as necessary for their safety or protection and as specified in the Service User Plan, based on assessment and with the individual's prior agreement.

Care homes offering accommodation to people who have physical disabilities or sensory impairments must ensure that suitable specialist adaptations and equipment are provided to meet individually assessed needs. Personal care facilities should meet the cultural requirements of the people who live in the home. While hygiene and control of infection are important, not all homes will be expected to provide, for example, sluicing facilities, disinfectors or special laundry rooms. Facilities and arrangements should be as home-like as possible while being demonstrably fit for the purpose of the home and for the people who live there.

The onus will be on proprietors to make clear the people for whom their homes are intended, and to make sure the physical environment matches their individual requirements. This section does not seek to set out detailed standards to meet the wide variety of needs of different user groups, though certain standards of provision common to all homes should be met. Proprietors will have to meet claims they make in their Statement of Purpose about the physical environment.

See also:

SENSE (2000), *Standards for Services for People who are Deafblind.*

RNIB & SIGN (1999), *Visibly Better.*

RADAR (1999), *The DDA 1995.*

CAE/NHS Estates (1998), *The Design of Residential and Nursing Homes.*

Public Health Medicine Environmental Group (1986), *Guidelines on Control of Infection.*

Health and Safety Executive (2001), *Health and Safety in Care Homes.*

Premises

OUTCOME

Service users live in a homely, comfortable and safe environment

STANDARD 24

24.1 **The home's premises are suitable for its stated purpose; accessible, safe and well-maintained; meet service users' individual and collective needs in a comfortable and homely way; and have been designed with reference to relevant guidance.**

24.2 Pre-existing care homes, which provided at least a minimum total average living space (bedroom and communal space) of 14.1sq metres (17.1sq metres for wheelchair users) as at 16 August 2002 continue to do so. Where they did not provide that amount of space as at that date, they provide each service user with at least the same average living space (bedroom and communal space) as they provided as at 31 March 2002. Such care homes set out in their statement of purpose and service user's guide, information about the space provided for each service user.

24.3 New homes accommodate a maximum of twenty people with no more than ten people sharing a staff group, a dining area and other common facilities (in specialist colleges, dining rooms are in keeping with similar non-specialist colleges); existing, larger homes are organised into clusters of up to ten people on this basis by 1st April 2007.

24.4 Homes intended for short-term, term-time education, or rehabilitation services for periods up to six months may have accommodation arrangements that are more flexible than that set out in Standard 24.3, if the accommodation remains domestic in scale and is consistent with the home's Statement of Purpose.

24.5 Service users on respite/emergency/short-term placements or intermediate care/rehabilitation placements, and those in long-term placements, occupy separate premises including communal day space, facilities and equipment, unless benefits for both groups can be demonstrated.

24.6 The premises are safe, comfortable, bright, cheerful, airy, clean and free from offensive odours, and provide sufficient and suitable light, heat and ventilation.

24.7 The home offers access to local amenities, local transport and relevant support services, to suit the personal and lifestyle needs of service users and the purpose of the home.

24.8 The premises are in keeping with the local community and have a style and ambience that reflect the home's purpose.

24.9 The premises are accessible to all service users. Homes accommodating wheelchair users provide level access, and doorways into communal areas, service users' rooms, bathing and toilet facilities and other spaces to which wheelchair users have access should be of a width sufficient to allow wheelchair users adequate access. In all new build, extensions and first time registrations doorways into areas to which wheelchair users have access should have a clear opening width of 800mm.

24.10 Furnishings, fittings, adaptations and equipment are good quality, and are as domestic, unobtrusive and ordinary as is compatible with fulfilling their purpose.

24.11 The premises meet the requirements of the local fire service and environmental health department, health and safety and building Acts and Regulations, and from 1st April 2004 the Disability Discrimination Act 1995 Part 3.

24.12 The home has a planned maintenance and renewal programme for the fabric and decoration of the premises, with records kept.

24.13 CCTV cameras are restricted to entrance areas for security purposes and do not impinge on the daily life of service users.

Individual Rooms: Space Requirements

OUTCOME

Service users' bedrooms suit their needs and lifestyles.

STANDARD 25

25.1 The registered person provides each service user with a bedroom which has useable floor space sufficient to meet individual needs and lifestyles.

25.2 All service users are offered the option of a single room.

25.3 Pre-existing care homes, with rooms which provided single rooms with at least 10 sq metres of useable floor space (12sq metres for wheelchair users) – excluding en-suite – as at 16 August 2002, continue to provide that amount of space in those rooms. Pre-existing care homes with rooms which did not provide that amount of space as at that date, provide at least the same useable floor space in those rooms as they provided as at 31 March 2002. Such care homes set out in their statement of purpose and service user's guide, information about the size of their single rooms.

25.4 Single rooms in current use accommodating wheelchair users and service users with complex nursing needs (e.g. ventilation/life support systems) have at least 12 sq m usable floor space, excluding en suite, providing sufficient additional space for turning, transferring and accessing belongings, and for medical equipment and nursing requirements.

25.5 In existing homes, service users share bedrooms only in accordance with the following conditions:

    i.   multiple occupancy is phased out by 1st April 2002;

    ii. Two service users make a positive choice to share.

    iii. shared rooms provide at least 16 sq m usable floor space, excluding en suite; and

    iv. in short stay homes for people who misuse substances, when a clinical need for sharing is established up to four people may share a room if privacy is assured through screening or the provision of furniture.

25.6 New build registrations and extensions intended for long-term placements provide individual en suite bedrooms with at least 12 sq m usable floor space (15 sq m for wheelchair users) excluding en suite.

25.7 First time registrations and extensions intended for placements of less than six months provide individual bedrooms with at least 10 sq m usable floor space (15 sq m for wheelchair users) excluding en suite.

25.8   In first time registrations and extensions, service users share bedrooms only in accordance with the following conditions:

   i.   two service users choose to share and, except in short stay homes, are offered two rooms to use – for example, as a bedroom and sitting room;

   ii.   a mixture of single and double rooms may be offered, on the basis of clinical need, for people who misuse substances.

Individual Rooms: Furniture and Fittings

OUTCOME

Service users' bedrooms promote their independence.

STANDARD 26

26.1   The registered person provides each service user with a bedroom that has furniture and fittings sufficient and suitable to meet individual needs and lifestyles.

26.2   Service users' bedrooms include (unless agreed otherwise in the person's individual Plan, or being identified as in their best interests):

   i.   bed, table, chest of drawers and two comfortable chairs;

   ii.   wardrobe/cupboard space and lockable storage space;

   iii. wash hand basin (unless en suite facilities provided);

   iv.   space for service users' usual possessions e.g. computer, music systems, personal electrical appliances, hoists/technical aids;

   v.   at least two double sockets, TV aerial point, and telephone point (or access to a cordless telephone handset for use in the room);

   vi.   bedding, curtains and floor covering of good quality and design suitable for the service user; and

   vii   a window which opens, at a level providing a view when seated; good lighting and ventilation; and individually controlled heating.

26.3   Service users can bring and/or choose (or are helped to choose) their own furniture and can decorate and personalise their rooms subject to fire and safety requirements.

26.4   Service users' bedrooms are lockable. Staff use an override device only as indicated by a service user's risk assessment.

Toilets and Bathrooms

OUTCOME

Service users' toilets and bathrooms provide sufficient privacy and meet their individual needs.

STANDARD 27

27.1 **The registered person provides service users with toilet and bathroom facilities which meet their assessed needs and offer sufficient personal privacy.**

27.2 Pre-existing care homes, which provided at least enough toilets so that they were shared by no more than three people as at 16 August 2002 continue to do so. Where they did not provide enough toilets to do that as at that date, they provide at least the same number of en-suite toilets, toilets and wash hand basins as they provided as at 31 March 2002. Such care homes set out in their statement of purpose and service user's guide, information about the number of en-suite toilets, toilets and wash hand basins they provide.

27.3 In new registrations and extensions, en suite toilets and hand basins are provided; where en suite facilities cannot be provided in new registrations of small, family-type homes a minimum of one toilet and one bath/shower are provided per two service users.

27.4 Pre-existing care homes, which provided at least enough bathrooms so that they were shared by no more that three people as at 16 August 2002 continue to do so. Where they did not provide enough bathrooms to do that as at that date, they provide at least the same number of bathrooms as they provided as at 31 March 2002. Such care homes set out in their statement of purpose and service user's guide, information about the number of bathrooms they provide.

27.5 Toilets and bathrooms, suitable for service users' specialist and cultural needs are located near to service users' bedrooms; accessible toilets are also near dining rooms and other communal areas.

27.6 Toilets and bathrooms are lockable. Staff use an override device only as indicated by a service user's risk assessment.

Shared Space

OUTCOME

Shared spaces complement and supplement service users' individual rooms.

STANDARD 28

28.1 A range of comfortable, safe and fully accessible shared spaces is provided both for shared activities and for private use.

28.2 Shared spaces include:

    i.   outdoor space proportionate to number of service users and staff on duty;

    ii.   kitchen and laundry facilities which are domestic in scale;

    iii.   in all new build and first time registrations, communal areas (e.g. for meals, social activities) of at least 4.1sq metres per service user;

    iv.   in all new build and first time registrations communal areas of at least 5.1 sq metres per service user with wheelchair/mobility aids;

    v.   a private area for e.g. visitors, consultations or treatment; and

    vi   a separate smoking area if the home does not have a no-smoking policy.

28.3 Staff are provided with adequate facilities including a safe place to store personal belongings and sleeping facilities when sleeping in.

Adaptations and Equipment

OUTCOME

Service users have the specialist equipment they require to maximise their independence.

STANDARD 29

29.1 The registered person ensures the provision of the environmental adaptations and disability equipment necessary to meet the home's stated purpose and the individually assessed needs of all service users.

29.2 Homes offering a service to people with physical disabilities provide specialist equipment as needed for each individual including for example:

    i.   moving equipment/overhead tracking for hoists;

    ii.   stair rails, passenger lifts, stair lifts if compliant with Health and Safety Executive guidance (e.g. manufactured to ISO 9386 and BS 5776);

    iii.   environmental control system;

    iv.   right and left handed rooms;

    v.   appropriate bathroom fittings/equipment;

    vi.   call alarm systems;

    vii.   lowered light switches, work surfaces, window openings; and

    viii.   storage/recharging facilities for wheelchairs/mobility equipment in a discrete/separate area.

29.3   Homes offering a service to people with sensory impairment provide specialist aids and adaptations as needed including for example:

    i.   loops/microphones/minicoms/textphones/videophone;

    ii.   additional and/or anti-glare lighting; colour contrasting;

    iii.   tactile symbols; varied textural surfaces;

    iv.   florescent or padded hazards/obstructions (where they cannot be removed);

    v.   computer for users' personal use; and

    vi.   TV with video recorder and subtitling facility/sign language.

29.4   Homes offering a service to people referred for intermediate care provide rehabilitation facilities sited in dedicated space, including equipment for therapies and treatment and equipment to promote activities of daily living and mobility.

29.5   Homes offering a service to minority ethnic service users provide bathrooms with culturally appropriate fittings/personal care facilities.

29.6   Provision of aids, adaptations and equipment follows assessment by, and meets the recommendations of, an occupational therapist or other suitably qualified specialist.

29.7   Safety systems and equipment are appropriate for people with mobility/sensory problems – e.g. flashing light fire alarms, magnetic fire doors.

29.8   The home makes satisfactory arrangements for the repair and maintenance of equipment in general or individual use, to ensure its continued safety.

Hygiene and Control of Infection

OUTCOME

The home is clean and hygienic.

STANDARD 30

30.1 **The premises are kept clean, hygienic and free from offensive odours throughout and systems are in place to control the spread of infection, in accordance with relevant legislation, published professional guidance and the purpose of the home.**

30.2 Laundry facilities are sited so that soiled articles, clothing and infected linen are not carried through areas where food is stored, prepared, cooked or eaten and do not intrude on service users.

30.3 Hand washing facilities are prominently sited in areas where infected material and/or clinical waste are being handled.

30.4 The laundry floor finishes are impermeable and these and wall finishes are readily cleanable.

30.5 Policies and procedures for control of infection include the safe handling and disposal of clinical waste; dealing with spillages; provision of protective clothing; handwashing.

30.6 The home has a sluicing facility where appropriate and, in care homes providing nursing, a sluicing disinfector.

30.7 Foul laundry is washed at appropriate temperatures (minimum 65° C for not less than 10 minutes) to thoroughly clean linen and control risk of infection.

30.8 Washing machines have the specified programming ability to meet disinfection standards (where applicable).

30.9 Services and facilities comply with the Water Supply (Water Fittings) Regulations 1999.

7

Staffing

INTRODUCTION TO STANDARDS 31 TO 36

Section 7 sets out standards for the provision and maintenance of a staff team with the qualities, qualifications, training and support required to meet the stated purpose of the home and the assessed needs of the people who live in it.

Probably the most important factor for younger adults living in care homes is the staff who work there. Service users who participated in the consultation workshops stressed the importance of staff who are accessible and approachable; good listeners and communicators; reliable and honest; interested and motivated; and competent to carry out the tasks required of them. Continuity and stability of staff support were a concern for many service users.

Many service users expressed frustration and anger about staff who do not listen to them or understand their needs regarding, for example, their disability, culture, communication problems or specialist programme. Service users stressed the importance of receiving support from staff who know, for example, their likes and dislikes, their preferred communication method or moving and transferring techniques, and how to use their disability equipment. Service users have a right to be supported by staff who respect them and their possessions, and their lifestyle choices and preferences, as detailed in the Service User Plan.

For care home managers, a quality workforce requires attention to issues of recruitment, training and development, skill mix and numbers, and supervision and support. The NMS require managers to ensure that staff understand the purpose of the home and the key values that underpin the standards. These standards require that staff have clear job descriptions linked to meeting service users' assessed needs and individual goals. Emphasis will be placed on developing staff training to meet Sector Skills Council workforce targets, and on supporting staff to gain qualifications meeting TOPSS specifications. These standards do not set detailed specifications for staffing levels and skill mixes. However the home should be able clearly to demonstrate that staff members individually, and the staff team as a whole, can meet service users' individual assessed needs and fulfil the stated purpose of the home. The Department of Health will be issuing guidance regarding registered nursing and care staff.

See also:

Residential Forum (1988), *Training for Social Care.*

G Bailey (2000), *Managers as Trainers.*

Leonard Cheshire and SCA (2000), *Social Care Practice Handbook.*

Roles

OUTCOME

Service users benefit from clarity of staff roles and responsibilities.

STANDARD 31

31.1 **The registered manager ensures that staff have clearly defined job descriptions and understand their own and others' roles and responsibilities.**

31.2 Staff know and support the main aims and values of the home, understand and implement the home's policies and procedures, and know how their work, and that of other staff (including key workers), promotes the main aims of the home.

31.3 Staff job descriptions are linked to achieving service users' individual goals as set out in the Service User Plan.

31.4 Staff get to know and develop a relationship with the service users they support, and are able to meet individual needs with particular attention to gender, age, cultural background and personal interests.

31.5 Staff are familiar with and comply with standards of conduct and practice set by the General Social Care Council (GSCC); nursing staff and all allied health professionals comply with the standards of conduct and practice established by their regulatory bodies.

31.6 Staff are aware of their own knowledge and skill limitations and know when it is appropriate to involve someone else with more specific expertise.

31.7 The contribution of volunteers supplements and does not replace paid staff roles; volunteers do not undertake tasks which are the responsibility of paid staff.

Qualities and Qualifications

OUTCOME

Service users are supported by competent and qualified staff.

STANDARD 32

32.1 **Staff have the competencies and qualities required to meet service users' needs and achieve Sector Skills Council workforce strategy targets within the required timescales.**

32.2 Staff respect service users and have attitudes and characteristics that are important to them. They are:

    i.   accessible to, approachable by, and comfortable with service users;

    ii.   good listeners and communicators;

    iii.   reliable and honest; and

    iv.   interested, motivated and committed.

32.3 Staff have the skills and experience necessary for the tasks they are expected to do, including:

    i.   knowledge of the disabilities and specific conditions of service users;

    ii.   specialist skills to meet service users' individual needs, including skills in communication and in dealing with anticipated behaviours;

    iii.   understanding of physical and verbal aggression and self-harm as a way of communicating needs, preferences and frustrations;

    iv.   understanding of the cultural and religious heritage of each service user;

    v.   techniques for rehabilitation including treatment and recovery programmes, the promotion of mobility, continence and self care, and outreach programmes to re-establish community living;

    vi.   appreciation of, and ability to balance, the particular and fluctuating needs of individuals and the needs of all service users; and

    vii.   professional relationships with e.g. GPs, social workers, nurses, psychiatrists, therapists and staff working in other care homes and community and specialist agencies.

32.4 Trainees (including all staff under 18) are registered on a Sector Skills Council standard training programme, work only under the direct supervision of qualified staff and do not undertake intimate personal care tasks.

32.5 Care staff hold a care NVQ 2 or 3 (or a nursing qualification if providing nursing care); are working to obtain one by an agreed date; or the registered manager can demonstrate that through past work experience staff meet that standard.

32.6 50% of care staff (including agency staff) in the home achieve a care NVQ 2 [by 2005].

Staff Team

OUTCOME

Service users are supported by an effective staff team.

STANDARD 33

33.1 The home has an effective staff team, with sufficient numbers and complementary skills to support service users' assessed needs at all times.

33.2 The numbers and skill mix of staff on duty (including domestic staff), day or night, ensure the following activities are carried out effectively and efficiently to meet the individual and collective needs of service users:

   i.   uninterrupted work with individuals;

   ii.   administration, organisation and communication;

   iii. day to day running of the home; and

   iv.   management of emergencies.

33.3 The ratios of care staff to service users must be determined according to the assessed needs of residents, and a system operated for calculating staff numbers required, in accordance with guidance recommended by the Department of Health.

33.4 Records show low rates of turnover and sick leave, and low use of agency/bank staff; where used, there is a core team of agency/bank staff who know the service users and understand the home's way of working.

33.5 Where indicated, specialist services are secured from relevant professions to support the assessed needs of service users (including physio-and occupational therapists in homes providing intermediate care/rehabilitation; and trained nurses in homes providing nursing care).

33.6 The staff team reflects the cultural/gender composition of service users.

33.7 Trainees (including all staff under 18) make up less than 20% of the total care hours and there is no more than one trainee on duty at any time.

33.8 Regular staff meetings take place (minimum six per year) and are recorded and actioned.

33.9 There are staff on duty at all times who can communicate with service users in their first language including sign; and have skills in other communication methods relevant to service users' needs (eg block alphabet, braille, finger spelling, Makaton, total communication, manual deafblind language, moon, personal symbols).

33.10 Staff providing intimate personal care for service users are at least age18; staff left in charge of the home are at least age 21.

33.11 Staffing levels are regularly reviewed to reflect service users' changing needs.

Recruitment

OUTCOME

Service users are supported and protected by the home's recruitment policy and practices.

STANDARD 34

34.1 **The registered person operates a thorough recruitment procedure based on equal opportunities and ensuring the protection of service users.**

34.2 Two written references are obtained before making an appointment and any gaps in the employment record explored.

34.3 New staff are confirmed in post only following completion of a satisfactory police check, satisfactory check of the Protection of Children and Vulnerable Adults and UKCC registers.

34.4 Service users are actively supported to be involved in staff selection, and are supported through the processes of joining and departure of staff.

34.5 Staff are employed in accordance with, and are given copies of, the codes of conduct and practice set by the GSCC.

34.6 All staff receive statements of terms and conditions.

34.7 All staff appointments are subject to a minimum three-month probationary period and service users are involved in their review.

34.8 The recruitment and selection of volunteers is thorough and includes police and POVA/POCA checks.

Training and Development

OUTCOME

Service users' individual and joint needs are met by appropriately trained staff.

STANDARD 35

35.1 **The registered person ensures that there is a staff training and development programme which meets Sector Skills Council workforce training targets and ensures staff fulfil the aims of the home and meet the changing needs of service users.**

35.2 The home has a training and development plan, dedicated training budget, and designated person with responsibility for the training and development programme.

35.3 All staff receive structured induction training (within six weeks of appointment) and foundation training (within six months of appointment) to Sector Skills Council specification (including training on the principles of care, safe working practices, the organisation and worker role, the experiences and particular needs of the service user group, and the influences and particular requirements of the service setting).

35.4 All staff receive equal opportunities training, including disability equality training provided by disabled trainers; and race equality and anti-racism training.

35.5 Each staff member has an individual training and development assessment and profile [by 2004], and at least five paid training and development days (pro rata) per year.

35.6 A training needs assessment is carried out for the staff team as a whole, and an impact assessment of all staff development is undertaken to identify the benefits for service users and to inform future planning.

35.7 Training and development are linked to the home's service aims and to service users' needs and individual Plans; and service users are involved in determining staff training needs and plans.

35.8 Staff working in learning disability services use Learning Disability Award Framework-accredited training to provide underpinning knowledge for progress towards achieving R/NVQs.

Supervision and Support

OUTCOME
Service users benefit from well supported and supervised staff.

STANDARD 36

36.1 Staff receive the support and supervision they need to carry out their jobs.

36.2 There are established arrangements for managers to brief staff, and for managers to receive direct feedback from staff.

36.3 Staff who supervise colleagues are trained, and are supported/supervised by senior staff.

36.4 Staff have regular, recorded supervision meetings at least six times a year with their senior/manager in addition to regular contact on day to day practice (fortnightly where there is no regular contact; pro-rata for part-time staff), covering:

    i.   translation of the home's philosophy and aims into work with individuals;

    ii.   monitoring of work with individual service users;

    iii. support and professional guidance; and

    iv. identification of training and development needs.

36.5   Staff have access to specialist supervision as indicated by service users' assessed needs.

36.6   Staff have an annual appraisal with their line manager to review performance against job description and agree career development plans.

36.7   Staff have copies of the home's written grievance and disciplinary procedures.

36.8   Procedures are in place for dealing with physical aggression towards staff (see also Standard 23 – "Protection").

8

Conduct and management of the home

INTRODUCTION TO STANDARDS 37 TO 43

The standards in Section 8 cover the policies, procedures and practices that must be carried out by the registered provider and/or manager in order to ensure that the care home fulfils it stated purpose and objectives, and meets the needs of the people who live there.

The calibre of the registered manager is critical to the quality of the care home. This section sets standards relating to the qualifications, responsibilities and training requirements of the registered manager that will ensure the effective day-to-day running of the home.

Proprietors/managers will be expected to have procedures in place, suitable for the size and purpose of the home, to ensure the short-and long-term viability of the home, including a business and financial plan.

The Standards for Care Homes for Adults (18–65) highlight the importance of listening to service users and involving them in all aspects of life in the home. A competent and skilled manager will foster an atmosphere of openness and respect, in which service users, family, friends and staff all feel valued and that their opinions matter. Care homes are required to have a quality assurance and quality monitoring system, including provision for asking service users for their opinions and publishing the results of this survey. It is not essential to subscribe to an external system although many providers do and there are good examples to choose from.

See also:

Residential Forum (1997), *Managing a Home from Home.*

Health and Safety Executive (1993), *Health and Safety in Residential Care Homes.*

J Burton (1998), *Managing Residential Care.*

C Payne (1994), *Evaluating Quality of Care.*

Day-to-Day Operations

OUTCOME

Service users benefit from a well run home.

STANDARD 37

37.1   **The registered manager is qualified, competent and experienced to run the home and meet its stated purpose, aims and objectives.**

37.2   The registered manager:

    i.   has at least two years significant management/supervisory experience in a relevant care setting within the past five years; and

    ii.   qualifications at level 4 NVQ in both management and care [by 2005]; OR

    iii.   where nursing care is provided by the home, is a first level registered nurse and has a level 4 NVQ in management [by 2005].

37.3   The registered manager has overall responsibility, set out in a job description, to ensure that:

    i.   written aims and objectives of the home are achieved;

    ii.   policies and procedures are implemented;

    iii.   the home's budget is properly managed;

    iv.   certificates and licenses are obtained and displayed;

    v.   each service user has a written contract/statement of terms and conditions and that the terms of the contract/statement are fulfilled; and

    vi.   the home complies with the Care Standards Act and Regulations, General Social Care Council codes of practice and other legal requirements.

37.4   The registered manager undertakes periodic training and development meeting TOPSS specifications, to maintain and update his/her knowledge, skills and competence while managing the home.

Ethos

OUTCOME

Service users benefit from the ethos, leadership and management approach of the home.

STANDARD 38

38.1   **The management approach of the home creates an open, positive and inclusive atmosphere.**

38.2   The registered manager communicates a clear sense of direction and leadership which staff and service users understand and are able to relate to the aims and purpose of the home.

38.3   The registered manager has strategies for enabling staff, service users and other stakeholders to voice concerns and to affect the way in which the service is delivered (see Standard 22 – "Concerns and complaints").

38.4   The processes of managing and running the home are open and transparent.

38.5   Management planning and practice encourage and reward innovation, creativity, development and change.

38.6   A commitment is made to equal opportunities in the organisation.

Quality Assurance

OUTCOME

Service users are confident their views underpin all self-monitoring, review and development by the home.

STANDARD 39

39.1   Effective quality assurance and quality monitoring systems, based on seeking the views of service users, are in place to measure success in achieving the aims, objectives and statement of purpose of the home.

39.2   There is an annual development plan for the home, based on a systematic cycle of planning-action-review, reflecting aims and outcomes for service users.

39.3   There is continuous self-monitoring, using an objective, consistently obtained and reviewed and verifiable method (preferably a professionally recognised quality assurance system) and involving service users; and an internal audit takes place at least annually.

39.4   The results of service user surveys are published and made available to service users, their representatives and other interested parties including the NCSC.

39.5   The registered manager and staff can demonstrate year on year development for each service user, linked to implementation of the individual Plan.

39.6   Feedback is actively sought from service users (with support from independent advocates as appropriate) about services provided through e.g. anonymous user satisfaction questionnaires and individual and group discussion, as well as evidence from records and life plans; and informs all planning and review.

39.7   The views of family, friends and advocates and of stakeholders in the community (e.g. GPs, teachers, chiropodist, audiologist, voluntary organisation staff) are sought on how the home is achieving goals for service users.

39.8 Service users are told about planned NCSC inspections and are given access to inspectors, in private, with interpreters/advocates as required, and the views of service users are made available to NCSC inspectors for inclusion in inspection reports.

39.9 Policies, procedures and practices are regularly reviewed in light of changing legislation and of good practice advice from the Department of Health, local/health authorities, and specialist/professional organisations.

39.10 Action is progressed within agreed timescales to implement requirements identified in NCSC inspection reports.

Policies and Procedures

OUTCOME

Service users' rights and best interests are safeguarded by the home's policies and procedures.

STANDARD 40

40.1 The home's written policies and procedures comply with current legislation and recognised professional standards, covering the topics set out in Appendix 3.

40.2 Policy statements are appropriate to the setting and cover:

i. general policy content;

ii. organisation for carrying out the policy; and

iii. arrangements for carrying out the policy.

40.3 Staff have access to up-to-date copies of, and understand and apply, all policies, procedures and codes of practice.

40.4 Service users have access to relevant policies, procedures and codes of practice, in appropriate formats, and staff have tried to explain them to service users.

40.5 Staff are fully involved in developing policies and procedures, and service users have opportunities to help in their formulation.

40.6 All policies, procedures, codes of practice and records are signed by the registered manager and are dated, monitored, reviewed and amended.

Record Keeping

OUTCOME

Service users' rights and best interests are safeguarded by the home's record keeping policies and procedures.

STANDARD 41

41.1 **Records required by regulation for the protection of service users and for the effective and efficient running of the business are maintained, up to date and accurate.**

41.2 Service users have access to their records and information about them held by the home, and opportunities to help maintain their personal records.

41.3 Individual records and home records are secure, up to date and in good order; and are constructed, maintained and used in accordance with the Data Protection Act 1998 and other statutory requirements.

Safe Working Practices

OUTCOME

The health, safety and welfare of service users are promoted and protected.

STANDARD 42

42.1 **The registered manager ensures so far as is reasonably practicable the health, safety and welfare of service users and staff.**

42.2 The registered manager ensures safe working practices including:

i. moving and handling: use of techniques for moving people and objects that avoid injury to services users or staff;

ii. fire safety – understanding of fire precautions equipment and fire escape routes with which the premises are provided and of the procedures to be adopted in the event of a fire alarm being raised;

iii. first aid – knowledge of how to deal with accidents and health emergencies, provision of a first aid box and a qualified first aider at all times, and recording of all cases;

iv. food hygiene – correct storage and preparation of food to avoid food poisoning; and

v. infection control – understanding and practice of measures to prevent spread of infection and communicable diseases.

42.3 The registered manager ensures the health and safety of service users and staff including:

i. safe storage and disposal of hazardous substances;

ii. regular servicing of boilers and central heating systems under contract by competent persons (e.g. members of Council of Registered Gas Installers (CORGI));

iii. maintenance of electrical systems and electrical equipment;

iv. regulation of water temperature, and design solutions to control risk of Legionella and risk from hot water/surfaces, based on assessment of the capabilities and needs of service users (i.e. temperature close to 43° C);

v. provision and maintenance of window restrictors, based on assessment of vulnerability of and risk to service users;

vi. maintenance of a safe environment including kitchen equipment and laundry machinery; outdoor steps and pathways; gardening equipment;

vii. security of the premises; and

viii. security of service users based on assessment of their vulnerability.

42.4 The registered manager ensures compliance with relevant legislation including:

i. Health and Safety at Work Act 1974;

ii. Management of Health and Safety at Work Regulations 1999;

iii. Workplace (Health, Safety and Welfare) Regulations 1992;

iv. Provision and Use of Work Equipment Regulations 1992;

v. Electricity at Work Regulations 1989;

vi. Health and Safety (First Aid) Regulations 1981;

vii. Control of Substances Hazardous to Health Regulations (COSHH) 1999;

viii. Manual Handling Operations Regulations 1992;

ix. Reporting of Injuries, Diseases and Dangerous Occurrences Regulations (RIDDOR) 1995;

x. Gas Safety (Installation and Use) Regulations 1998;

xi. The Personal Protective Equipment at Work Regulations 1992;

xii. Health and Safety (Display Screen Equipment) Regulations 1992; and

xiii Fire Precautions Act 1971 and Fire Precautions (Workplace) Regulations 1997 as amended.

42.5 The registered manager provides a written statement of the policy, organisation and arrangements for maintaining safe working practices.

42.6 The registered manager ensures that risk assessments are carried out for all safe working practice topics covered in Standards 42.2 and 42.3, and that significant findings of the risk assessment are recorded.

42.7 All accidents, injuries, incidents of illness or communicable disease, or the death of a service user, are recorded and reported.

42.8 Safety procedures are posted, and explained, in formats that are easily understood and take account of service users' special communication needs.

42.9 All staff receive induction and foundation training and updates to meet TOPSS specification on all safe working practice topics in Standards 42.2 and 42.3 (see Standard 35.3 – 'Training and development').

Conduct of the Service

OUTCOME

Service users benefit from competent and accountable management of the service.

STANDARD 43

43.1 The overall management of the service (within or external to the home) ensures the effectiveness, financial viability and accountability of the home.

43.2 There is a business and financial plan for the home and the service, open to NCSC inspection and reviewed annually.

43.3 Systems are in place to ensure:

i. financial planning, budget monitoring and financial control;

ii. human resources planning including assurance of financial acumen;

iii. selection, training, supervision and appraisal of registered managers; and

iv. quality monitoring.

43.4 Insurance cover is put in place against loss or damage to the assets of the business. The level of cover should reflect the full replacement value of buildings, fixture, fittings and equipment.

43.5 Insurance cover is provided for business interruption costs (including loss of earnings) as well as costs to the operator of meeting its contract liabilities. The latter must be sufficient to cover the registered person's legal liabilities to employees, service users and third party persons to a limit commensurate with the level and extent of activities undertaken or to a minimum of £5 million.

43.6   Service users are involved where possible in the business and financial planning and monitoring of the home.

43.7   Lines of accountability within the home, and with any external management, are clearly understood by staff and service users.

National Minimum Standards for Care Homes for Adults (18–65) – Supplementary Standards for care homes accommodating young people aged 16 and 17

Introduction

The Adults (18–65) Standards and outcomes apply to care homes accommodating 16 and 17 year olds during their transition to adulthood. The Supplementary Standards set out in this section cover the needs of younger people aged 16 and 17 years. The first part of the Standard mirrors the relevant Standard set out in the Adult (18–65) Standards and is in italics to highlight the fact that it is not a new standard. The paragraphs in normal type reflect the Supplementary Standards that should be applied.

It is expected that the registration of care homes that are to take 16 and 17 year olds will be conditional on the homes accommodating 16–25 year olds only. Care homes should not accommodate children under the age of 16.

1

Choice of home

Information

STANDARD 1

1.1 *The registered person produces an up-to-date statement of purpose setting out the aims, objectives and philosophy of the home, its services and facilities, and terms and conditions; and provides each prospective service user with a service users' guide to the home.*

In addition to the requirements in Standards 1.1–1.4, homes accommodating young people aged 16 and 17 meet the following supplementary standard:

1.5 The statement of purpose describes what the home sets out to do specifically for young people aged 16 and 17, and including arrangements for leaving care/the transition to adulthood.

Needs Assessment

STANDARD 2

2.1 *New service users are admitted only on the basis of a full assessment undertaken by people competent to do so, involving the prospective service user using an appropriate communication method and with an independent advocate as appropriate.*

In addition to the requirements in Standards 2.1–2.8, homes accommodating young people aged 16 and 17 meet the following supplementary standard:

2.9 The registered person ensures that each young person has a placement plan which sets out assessed needs, the objectives of the placement, and how these are to be met by the registered provider on a day-to-day basis, the contribution to be made by the staff of the home, and how the effectiveness of the placement is to be assessed.

2

Individual needs and choices

Service User Plan

STANDARD 6

6.1 ***The registered manager develops and agrees with each service user an individual Plan, which may include treatment and rehabilitation, describing the services and facilities to be provided by the home, and how these services will meet current and changing needs and aspirations and achieve goals.***

In addition to the requirements in Standards 6.1–6.10, homes accommodating young people aged 16 and 17 meet the following supplementary standards:

6.11 The registered manager contributes effectively to each child's placement review and child in care review and ensures the implementation of the agreed outcome of reviews as necessary.

6.12 The home contacts placing authorities to request emergency and statutory reviews when due, if the placing authority has not arranged the review; and the results of all statutory reviews are recorded in the service user's individual file, with individuals responsible for pursuing actions arising from reviews clearly identified.

6.13 The registered manager, in agreement with the placing authority, implements the Leaving Care Plan, consistent with the placement plan/Service User Plan, and where applicable the care or pathway plan, for any young person who expects to leave care or move to independent living within the next year. This plan outlines the support and assistance the service user will receive to enable successful transition to adulthood, including arrangements for:

i. education, training and employment;

ii. securing safe and affordable accommodation;

iii. support necessary for disabled young people;

iv. financial assistance to enable the young person to set up and maintain independent accommodation if applicable;

v. claiming welfare benefits where this is identified as a need;

vi. general and specialised health education and health care, and other specialist services such as counselling; and

vii. maintaining existing support networks as defined by the young person and creating new networks.

Risk Taking

STANDARD 9

9.1 *Staff enable service users to take responsible risks, ensuring they have good information on which to base decisions, within the context of the service user's individual Plan and of the home's risk assessment and risk management strategies.*

In addition to the requirements in Standards 9.1–9.4, homes accommodating young people aged 16 and 17 meet the following supplementary standard:

9.5 Any high risk activity provided or arranged is supervised by persons qualified to supervise involvement in the activity concerned (such as the qualification for instructing or supervising children awarded by the recognised national body for the activity concerned).

3

Lifestyle

Personal Development

STANDARD 11

11.1 *Staff enable service users to have opportunities to maintain and develop social, emotional, communication and independent living skills.*

In addition to the requirements in Standards 11.1–11.4, homes accommodating young people aged 16 and 17 meet the following supplementary standard:

11.5 The home helps service users prepare for leaving care, including:
   i.   developing and maintaining social and sexual relationships;
   ii. developing self esteem;
   iii. developing practical, daily life knowledge and skills; and
   iv. preparing for the world of work and for coping with unemployment and/or isolation.

Education and Occupation

STANDARD 12

12.1 *Staff help service users to find and keep appropriate jobs, continue their education or training, and/or take part in valued and fulfilling activities.*

In addition to the requirements in Standards 12.1–12.6, homes accommodating young people aged 16 and 17 meet the following supplementary standards:

12.7 Each service user's individual plan contains details of educational history, progress and achievements, and relevant reports (such as the Personal Education Plan).

12.8 The individual plan explicitly addresses the service user's education (including school, further or higher education) and covers:
   i.   whether the service user's needs will be met by attending a particular educational establishment;
   ii. any special educational needs and how they will be met;
   iii. promoting school (or college) attendance;
   iv. parental/social worker involvement in education;
   v.   dates of national examinations such as GCSE, AS, and A levels;

vi.   arrangements for travelling to and from school;

vii. staff with responsibility for liaising with schools, careers service, job centre employment agencies and local employers as appropriate; and

viii. further education, training and employment of each service user over school age.

12.9   Staff are familiar with the educational histories and the educational needs of young people in the home.

12.10 Service users are given full access to education facilities, and are provided with facilities that are conducive to study, and are encouraged to do homework and given help if they wish.

12.11 Staff (usually the key worker) attend parents' meetings and other school events which are normally attended by parents.

Leisure

STANDARD 14

14.1   Staff ensure that service users have access to, and choose from, a range of appropriate leisure activities.

In addition to the requirements in Standards 14.1–14.6, homes accommodating young people aged 16 and 17 meet the following supplementary standards:

14.7   Birthdays, name days, cultural and religious festivals are celebrated and service users participate in planning these events.

14.8   Activities provide a balance between free and controlled time, are experiential, and provide a mix of time with and without adults.

14.9   Service users under the age of 18 do not have access to, or watch videos certified as suitable for over 18s, and systems and policies are in place to safeguard service users when computer networking or on the Internet.

14.10 Leisure interests and areas in which a service user has talents or abilities are encouraged and financially supported.

Meals

STANDARD 17

17.1   The registered person promotes service users' health and wellbeing by ensuring the supply of nutritious, varied, balanced and attractively presented meals in a congenial setting and at flexible times.

In addition to the requirements in Standards 17.1–17.9, homes accommodating young people aged 16 and 17 meet the following supplementary standard:

17.10 The home seeks medical advice if a service user consistently refuses to eat, and for those who over-eat or have any other eating disorders.

4

Personal support

Health Care

STANDARD 19

19.1 ***The registered person ensures that the healthcare needs of service users are assessed and recognised and that procedures are in place to address them.***

In addition to the requirements in Standards 19.1–19.5, homes accommodating young people aged 16 and 17 meet the following supplementary standards:

19.6 The home provides guidance, advice and support on alcohol and illegal substance abuse, smoking, sex education, HIV infection, hepatitis and sexually transmitted diseases.

19.7 Staff do not smoke with or in the presence of children accommodated in the home. Only in particular circumstances and with the registered provider's express permission do staff have a small alcoholic drink whilst on duty (e.g. Christmas lunch). Under no circumstances does a member of staff use any illegal drug or other substance in the home nor does a member of staff take any such substance into the home.

5

Concerns, complaints and protection

Protection

STANDARD 23

23.1 *The registered person ensures that service users are safeguarded from physical, financial or material, psychological or sexual abuse, neglect, discriminatory abuse or self-harm or inhuman or degrading treatment, through deliberate intent, negligence or ignorance, in accordance with written policy.*

In addition to the requirements in Standards 23.1–23.6, homes accommodating young people aged 16 and 17 meet the following supplementary standards:

23.7　There are systems in place to promote the safety and welfare of children and to ensure that children are protected from abuse, which are known and understood by all staff (including junior, ancillary, volunteer and agency staff).

23.8　A copy of the local Area Child Protection Committee (ACPC) procedures is kept in the home. The registered manager of the home ensures that staff have read these, understand and are knowledgeable about them.

23.9　There are clear procedures, which are known, understood and followed by all staff, for responding to allegations or suspicions of abuse, either by staff or by other children in the home, or by others. They include:

　　i.　the requirement that staff or others working at the home who receive an allegation of abuse, or who suspect abuse, should avoid asking leading questions or giving inappropriate guarantees of confidentiality;

　　ii.　the requirement to report to the police any evidence of children becoming involved in prostitution, or of unauthorised persons picking children up, contacting children in the home, or observed trying to make contact with children outside the home; and

　　iii.　instructions for staff on action to be taken if an allegation or suspicion of abuse becomes known to them involving the registered manager or person at the time in day-to-day charge of the home.

23.10　The child protection procedures are in line with the local policies and procedures agreed by the Area Child Protection Committee (ACPC) relevant to the geographical area where the home is situated. The child protection procedures have been submitted for consideration and comment to the local ACPC, and any comments taken into account.

23.11 The registered manager has liaised with the local Social Services Department's Child Protection Co-ordinator (or other senior officer responsible for child protection matters in that department) to seek advice about local procedures and practice, and has discussed how the practices in the home relate to these regarding keeping children safe, responding to allegations or suspicions of abuse, methods of control and risk taking. Any conflicts between locally agreed procedures and those of other placing authorities have also been discussed.

23.12 There is written guidance for staff which makes clear the ways in which the registered manager of the home will ensure that members of staff subject to allegations against them will have access to information and support whilst an investigation ensues.

23.13 Procedural guidance for staff clearly demonstrates the systems required in order to protect children and minimise the risk of abuse whilst the child is living in the home. This includes guidance on:

    i.   making a full assessment of children's histories and any experience of abuse;

    ii.   observing contacts between children;

    iii.   supervision of children;

    iv.   supervision and support of staff;

    v.   recognition of possible involvement of children in prostitution;

    vi.   confidentiality;

    vii.   physical contact between staff and children;

    viii. one to one time alone by staff with children;

    ix.   intimate care and invasive procedures; and

    x.   administering medication.

23.14 The registered person ensures the provision of training for all staff, including ancillary staff, agency staff and volunteers, in the prevention of abuse, recognition of abuse (including its recognition in non-verbal children), dealing with disclosures or suspicions of abuse, and the home's child protection procedures. This training is included in induction programmes for new staff, including temporary or agency staff, and is ongoing for the staff group in keeping with the aims and objectives of the home.

23.15 The registered manager and staff have routine links with other agencies concerned with child protection, e.g. the placing authority, schools, hospitals, general practitioners, etc. and do not work in isolation from them.

23.16 The registered manager follows any local interagency protocols on prevention and investigation of child prostitution.

Countering Bullying

23.17 The home has, and follows, a policy on countering bullying which is known to service users and staff, which includes:

i. a definition of bullying, which is reviewed frequently with staff and service users, and which includes bullying by staff and bullying that may occur elsewhere than in the home and which covers different types of bullying, e.g. on the grounds of race, gender, disability or sexual orientation, and which includes name-calling;

ii. measures to prevent bullying and to respond to observed or reported bullying;

iii. training for staff in awareness of, and effective strategies to counter, bullying.

23.18 Service users who are bullied are supported, and those who may bully others are given suitable guidance.

Absence without Authority

23.19 The written procedures of the home identifying action to be taken when a child is absent without authority cover the following areas:

i. searching for any child missing or believed to have run away from the home;

ii. reporting missing children to the police, to the child's placing authority, and to others (including parents) subject to consultation with the placing authority;

iii. action to obtain information about the whereabouts of a missing child and to try to ensure the safety and welfare of that child;

iv the collection and return of missing children when found; and

v. action to be taken on the child's return, allowing for any individual arrangements based on the needs of the child as agreed in his/her residential plan.

6

Environment

Individual Rooms

STANDARD 25

25.1 ***The registered person provides each service user with a bedroom which has useable floor space sufficient to meet individual needs and lifestyles.***

In addition to the requirements in Standards 25.1–25.8, homes accommodating young people aged 16 and 17 meet the following supplementary standards:

25.9 Students living in specialist colleges may share a double room.

25.10 Service users do not share bedrooms with others of significantly different age (other than, by choice, with siblings following assessment of risk), or with those of the opposite sex.

25.11 The home provides facilities for children to study, which are quiet, with sufficient seating and desk or table space, adequately lit, with adequate storage for books and study materials, and available when needed for study purposes.

Staffing

Qualities and Qualifications

STANDARD 32

32.1 ***Staff have the competencies and qualities required to meet service users' needs and achieve Sector Skills Council workforce strategy targets within the required timescales.***

In addition to the requirements in Standards 32.1–32.6, homes accommodating young people aged 16 and 17 meet the following supplementary standard:

32.7 80% of care staff working with service users aged 16 and 17 have completed the level 3 Caring for Children and young People NVQ by 1st April 2005 or are working to achieve this qualification.

Staff Team

STANDARD 33

33.1 ***The home has an effective staff team, with sufficient numbers and complementary skills to support users' assessed needs at all times.***

In addition to the requirements in Standards 33.1–33.11, homes accommodating young people aged 16 and 17 meet the following supplementary standard:

33.12 Staff left in charge of young people aged 16 and 17 are aged at least 21.

Training and Development

STANDARD 35

35.1 ***The registered person ensures that there is a staff training and development programme which meets Sector Skills Council workforce training targets and ensures staff fulfil the aims of the home and meet the changing needs of service users.***

In addition to the requirements in Standards 35.1–35.8, homes accommodating young people aged 16 and 17 meet the following supplementary standard:

35.9 Induction training for staff who work with service users aged 16 and 17 includes guidance on child protection.

8 Conduct and management of the home

Record Keeping

STANDARD 41

41.1 *Records required by regulation for the protection of service users and for the effective and efficient running of the business are maintained, up to date and accurate.*

In addition to the requirements in Standards 41.1–41.3, homes accommodating young people aged 16 and 17 meet the following supplementary standard:

41.4 Individual records of service users aged 16 and 17 contain the additional information required by Children's Homes Regulations Schedule 3.

Appendices

Glossary – Care Homes for Adults (18–65)

Abuse

Single or repeated act or lack of appropriate action occurring within any relationship where there is an expectation of trust which causes harm or distress to an individual, including physical, emotional, verbal, financial, sexual or racial abuse, and neglect or abuse through the misapplication of drugs.

Assessment

Collection and interpretation of data to determine an individual's need for health, personal and social care and support services, undertaken with the individual, his/her representative and relevant professionals.

Care Home

An establishment providing accommodation with personal or nursing care.

Care Management

A system for organising the management and delivery of care services to vulnerable adults by local authority social services departments, and by CPNs, psychiatrists and other NHS personnel under Care Programme Approach (CPA) for people with mental health problems, involving assessing needs, care planning, organisation of care packages, monitoring and review, and close involvement with users and carers.

Care Programme Approach (CPA)

The formal process (integrated with Care Management) of assessing needs for services for people with mental health problems prior to and after discharge from hospital.

Care Plan

A written statement, regularly updated, setting out the health and social care services that a service user receives through Care Management, and how it is organised and delivered.

Contract

A written agreement between the service user and the home setting out the terms and conditions, and rights and responsibilities, of both parties, and including the Service User Plan.

First Time Registration

For the purposes of applying the standards, care homes which were in use immediately before April 2002 but were previously exempt from registration, such as "Royal Charter" homes and local authority homes, will NOT be treated as first time registrations and will only have to meet the "normal" standards.

Independent Advocate

An individual who is independent of the home or of any of the statutory agencies involved in the purchasing and provision of care in, or regulation of, the care home, who acts on behalf of and in the interests of a service user who feels unable to represent him/herself when dealing with professionals. Self-advocates are trained and supported to represent their own views.

Intermediate Care

A short period (normally no longer than six weeks) of intensive rehabilitation and treatment to enable service users to return home following (or to avoid) hospitalisation, or to prevent admission to long term care.

Keyworker

The person (who may be a designated nurse for people receiving nursing care) responsible for co-ordinating the service user's plan, for monitoring its progress and for staying in regular contact with the service user and everyone involved.

Leaving Care Plan

A plan to help young people make the transition from being looked after to independence.

Local Area Child Protection Committee

A group set up to determine the particular problems, policies and procedures concerning child protection in a given area.

Outcome

The end result of the service provided by a care home to a service user, which can be used to measure the effectiveness of the service.

Passenger Lift

A vertical means of transport between floors. A chair/stair lift is not a passenger lift.

Personal Care

Includes assistance with bodily functions where required.

Personal Education Plan

A plan which outlines the support a young person will receive for his/her education.

Physical Intervention

A method of responding to violence or aggressive behaviour which involves a degree of direct physical force to limit or restrict movement or mobility.

Policy

An operational statement of intent which helps staff make sound decisions and take actions which are legal, consistent with the aims of the home, and in the best interests of service users.

Pre-existing Care Home

For the purposes of applying the standards a pre-existing care home is one which existed immediately before 1 April 2002, whether or not registered under the Registered Homes Act 1984.

Procedure

The steps taken to fulfil a policy.

Registered Manager – see Registered Person

Registered Person

A person who either: carries on the home and is registered with the National Care Standards Commission to do so (the registered provider); or manages the home and is registered with the National Care Standards Commission to do so (the registered manager). In some cases, the registered provider may also manage the home.

Registered Provider – see Registered Person

Representative

A person acting on behalf of a service user, who may be a relative or friend.

Service User

Person living in and provided with services by a care home. Includes people who have physical disability, sensory impairment, learning disability, autistic spectrum disorder, mental health problems, substance misuse problems, HIV/AIDS, and/or dual or complex multiple disabilities including people who are deafblind.

Service User Plan

A Plan – generated from the single Care Management assessment where applicable – developed by the home with the service user, describing the services and facilities to be provided by the home and how these services will meet assessed needs and achieve personal goals.

Staff

Person working for pay within or from the home, full time, part time, casual or contract.

Standard

A measure by which quality is judged.

TOPSS

The Sector Skills Council for Social Care.

Usable Floor Space

Space which is accessible to the service user for furniture, possessions and daily living, with attention to e.g. room shape, positioning of doors, windows or en suite facilities, and headroom.

Volunteer

Person working without pay, or for expenses only, within or from the home.

Wheelchair User

A person whose main source of independent mobility is a wheelchair.

Policies and Procedures

Care homes will develop policies, procedures and/or codes of practice, appropriate to the setting, on the following topics:

- Absence without authority
- Adult protection and prevention of abuse
- Aggression towards staff
- Bullying
- Communicable diseases and infection control (Public Health Medicine Environmental Group guidelines)
- Concerns and complaints
- Confidentiality and disclosure of information
- Contact with/visits by family and friends
- Control of exposure to hazardous waste (COSSH)
- Control, administration, recording, safekeeping, handling and disposal of medicines including non-compliance
- Discharge, including planned discharge, and termination or self-discharge at short notice.
- Emergency admission and detention (Mental Health Act 1983) Emergencies and crises
- Equal opportunities and race equality (Race Relations Act 1996; Sex Discrimination Act 1975 & 1986; Disability Discrimination Act 1995)
- Fire safety
- Food safety and nutrition
- Health and safety (Health and Safety at Work Act 1974)
- Hygiene and food safety (Food Safety Act 1990 and Regulations 1995)
- Individual planning and review
- Induction and foundation training
- Management of service users' money and financial affairs
- Nursing/treatment/guardianship under Mental Health Act/Regulations 1983 and Mental Health Act Code of Practice 1983
- Physical intervention
- Racial harassment occurring between service users; between staff; by staff; or by service users on staff
- Record keeping and access to files
- Recruitment and employment including redundancy
- Referral and admission
- Risk assessment and management
- Sexuality and relationships
- Smoking, and use of alcohol and substances by users, visitors and staff
- Staff grievances and disciplinary action
- Whistle blowing
- Working with volunteers

Bibliography

Organisational Standards for Alcohol and Drug Treatment: Alcohol Concern and Drugscope

Bailey, G (1998) *Action Against Abuse: Recognising and preventing abuse of people with learning disabilities.* Chesterfield: ARC.

Bailey, G (2000) *Managers as Trainers: Supporting managers of services for people with learning disabilities to identify and meet staff development needs.* Chesterfield: ARC.

British Institute of Learning Disabilities & The National Autistic Society (1996) *Physical Interventions: a policy framework.* London: BILD and The National Autistic Society.

Burton, J (1998) *Managing Residential Care.* London: Routledge.

Campaign For Real Education (1995) *Racial equality means business: a standard for racial equality for employers.* London: CRE.

Care Standards Act 2000. London: TSO.

Centre for Accessible Environments/NHS Estates (1998) *The Design of Residential and Nursing Homes for Older People* (Health Facilities Notes HFN19). Leeds: NHS Estates on behalf of CAE. Data Protection Act 1998. London: TSO.

Department of Health (2002) *Guidance on the use of restrictive physical interventions for staff working with children and adults with learning disability and/or autism.* London: Department of Health.

Department of Health and Home Office (2000) *No Secrets: Guidance on developing and implementing multi-agency policies and procedures to protect vulnerable adults from abuse.* London: Department of Health.

Department of Health (1998) *Modernising Social Services: Promoting Independence, Improving Protection, Raising Standards.* London: TSO.

Department of Health (2001) V*aluing People: A new strategy for learning disability for the 21st century.* London: TSO.

Department of Health and Social Security (1975): *Residential accommodation for physically handicapped people,* LASSL (75) 19. London: DHSS.

Department of Health and Social Security and Scottish Office (1991), *Care Management and Assessment: Managers' Guide and Practitioners' Guide.* London.

Department of Health (2000) *Community Care (Direct Payments) Act 1996: Policy and practice guidance.* London.

Department of Health *Guidance on the Single Assessment Process for Older People: HSC2002/001: LAC (2002)1:* Issued 28 January 2002

Diabetic Association (July 1999) *Guidelines of practice for residents with diabetes in care homes.* London: Diabetic Association.

Dowson, S (1990) *Keeping it Safe: Self-advocacy by people with learning difficulties and the professional response.* London: Values Into Action.

Fitton, P (1994) *Listen to Me: Communicating the needs of people with profound intellectual and multiple disabilities.* London: Jessica Kinglsey.

Health and Safety Executive (2001) *Health and Safety in Care Homes (HSG220).* Sudbury: Health and Safety Executive.

Leonard Cheshire and Social Care Association (2000) *Social Care Practice Handbook.* London.

McIntosh, B and Whittaker, A (eds) (1988) *Days of Change: A practical guide to developing better day opportunities for people with learning difficulties.* London: King's Fund.

Mental Health Foundation (1996) *Building Expectations: Opportunities and services for people with a learning disability.* London: MHF.

Morris, J (2000) *Hurtling Into the Void.* Brighton: Pavilion.

Morris, J (2001) *'That Kind of Life': Social exclusion and young disabled people with high levels of support need.* Scope: London, with funding from the Community Fund.

Multiple Sclerosis Society and Leonard Cheshire Foundation (1998) *People with MS in long-term care: good practice guidelines for service providers.* London: MS Society.

National Council for Hospice and Specialist Palliative Care Services (1977) *Changing Gear: Guidelines for managing the last days of life in adults.* London: NCHSPC.

Office of Fair Trading (1998) *Choosing a Care Home.*

Payne, C (1994) E*valuating Quality of Care.* London: NSW.

Public Health Medicine Environment Group (1996) *Guidelines on the Control of Infection in Residential and Nursing Homes.* London: Department of Health.

Residential Forum (1997) *Managing 'A Home from Home': a Companion to 'Creating a Home from Home* – A Guide to Standards. London: Residential Forum.

Residential Forum (1998) *Training for Social Care: Achieving Standards for the Undervalued Service: A report on the Training and Staff Development for People Working in the Residential Care of Adults.* London: NISW.

Royal National Institute of the Blind: *National Visual Impairment Standards. Progress in Sight.* Issued by the Association of Directors of Social Services (ADSS): October 2002.

Royal National Institute for Deaf People (1999) *Best Practice Standards: Social Services for Deaf and Hard of Hearing People.* London: RNID.

Royal National Institute of the Blind (1999) *Visibly better: RNIB accreditation for residential and nursing homes.* London: RNIB.

Royal Pharmaceutical Society of Great Britain (1991) *Pharmaceutical Services to Nursing Homes.* London: Royal Pharmaceutical Society of Great Britain.

Sense, The National Deafblind and Rubella Association (2000) *Standards for services for adults who are deafblind or have a dual sensory impairment.* London: Sense.

Simons, K (1996) *I'm Not Complaining, But: A training pack on complaints procedures for everyone involved in community care services.* Brighton: Pavilion Press.

Social Services Inspectorate (1997) *Residential care for people with drug/alcohol problems: a report of a consultative project.* London: SSI.

The Royal Association for Disability and Rehabilitation (1999) *The Disability Discrimination Act 1995: a guide to the goods and services provisions.* DDA Guide Three. London: RADAR.

UKCC (1992) *Standards for the Administration of Medicines.* London: UKCC.

Values into Action (2001), *Who's in control? Decision-making by people with learning difficulties who have high support needs.* London: VIA.

Wertheimer, A (1996) *Changing Days: Developing new day opportunities with people who have learning difficulties.* London: King's Fund.

Wertheimer, A (1998) *Citizen Advocacy: A powerful partnership* (2nd edition). London: CAIT.